PRAISE

The Tapping Tool

"*The Tapping Tool* offers a very concrete and practical way to reduce stress, worry, and anxiety with a science backed, proven technique. Not only will you learn how to reduce stress, but the easy to follow processes offered by Tijana means everyone can benefit from this book—young and old. I truly recommend reading and applying *The Tapping Tool!*"

–DR. PETA STAPLETON, Associate Professor, Bond University and author of *The Science Behind Tapping* (Hay House)

"Simple is not always easy. However, Tijana masterfully teaches us how to employ this simple tool easily and effectively. While steeped in science and evidence-based research, her work is both practical and assessable. *The Tapping Tool* is an invaluable resource for school staff, social workers, or anyone who wants to learn how to implement self-regulation and mindfulness strategies."

–DEB ROBISON, MA, LSW, Director of Outreach and Collaboration Ohio's School-Based Center of Excellence for Prevention & Early Intervention, Miami University

"I've dedicated my career to leading nonprofits that serve children and families who've experienced significant trauma. The teams I've led, have experienced significant secondary trauma. Research suggests using a somatic tool to address trauma. I haven't found anything as easy to use, duplicatable, or effective as Functional Tapping. Tijana makes it so simple to use. It's been a game-changer."

–SHERRI MCKINNEY-FRANTZ, MAOL, LSW, CEO Blue Ridge CASA for Children

"You don't have to be a mental health professional to benefit from using this book. Fascinating, empowering, and comprehensive in scope, this valuable work offers hope for the millions seeking meaningful treatment and relief from the ongoing pain of trauma and anxiety. Tapping can change so much in your life. You don't have to stay stuck in fear and anxiety. Tijana walks you through this powerful technique in a quick, easy fashion. So please do yourself a big favor and read it to gain emotional freedom."

—MARTI MURPHY, creator of the Transformational Tapping Certification, emotional fitness coach, author of *Forbidden Emotions—The Key to Heal & 365 Days to Embracing Forbidden Emotions*

"Tijana's passionate and practical nature unites to deliver tapping instructions that make Functional Tapping accessible and repeatable for everyone! I use it all the time. Personally and professionally. It gives me a moment of pause to help me check in with my emotional reaction and what is really going on! This book is a practical tool for personal and professional use."

—LOUISE PROFIT, licensed social worker, certified trauma professional, and certified imago relationship therapist

"Functional Tapping is far easier and quicker than the traditional tapping I first learned. The way Tijana teaches it makes it super easy to learn and use. I've shared her teachings with many adults and children, many of whom have trauma histories. The results are usually immediate and noticeable. I highly recommend her book and courses to anyone who wants to be less stressed and more focused, and to heal triggers from simple bad habits and pet peeves to deeper issues."

—JODY JOHNSTON PAWEL, LSW, CFLE, CTSS, author of *The Parents Toolshop®: The Universal Blueprint® for Building a Healthy Family*

Important Note

This book provides information to raise awareness about the potential benefits of learning and applying EFT. However, readers must acknowledge their responsibility when utilizing this information. The content within this book is meant for general knowledge. It should not be seen as a replacement for conventional medical care provided by a qualified mental or medical healthcare specialist.

EFT and the information provided here are not meant to diagnose, treat, cure, or prevent any illnesses or conditions. If, during your EFT practice, you feel overwhelmed, distressed, or start recalling previously forgotten memories, it is advisable to consider seeking professional assistance from an experienced EFT Practitioner or a mental health expert. Before making any changes to your diet, medication, or healthcare plan, it is prudent to consult a qualified medical professional. By continuing to read this book, you are considered to have acknowledged and accepted the terms of this disclaimer.

THE
TAPPING
TOOL

A Guide for Outsmarting Stress &
Bringing Your Thinking Brain Back Online

TIJANA COSO

Published by Kahlua Press

Paperback ISBN: 979-8-9891584-0-9
eBook ISBN: 979-8-9891584-1-6

Book design by Olivia M. Hammerman

To my parents. I am blessed to have been built on the foundation of two rocks.

Definition

The Emotional Freedom Techniques (EFT), or Tapping, is an evidence-based therapeutic counseling intervention incorporating exposure, cognitive therapy, and somatic-stimulation elements. It alleviates stress and anxiety by stimulating specific acupuncture meridian points on the body through tapping, pressure, or rubbing while focusing on particular thoughts or emotions.

Contents

Introduction

I discovered Tapping while tossing in bed, unable to sleep.

Tapping saved me when my ideal life was ripped away and replaced by loneliness, depression, and the occasional suicidal thought. An unwelcome divorce after twenty-five years of what I thought was a good marriage can have that effect. I was not the only person shocked by this turn of events: neither my children, family nor friends saw it coming.

As the reality of my situation bore down on me, I turned my pain inward. Eventually, depression took over, and I couldn't function. At fifty-one, I was sad, scared, and struggling to move on.

If you have never been depressed, you might not understand the brain fog and apathy that cloud your senses and make even the simplest everyday tasks daunting. When my most honest and trusted friends repeatedly recommended counseling, I envisioned months of therapy. Since I didn't have a job or medical insurance, I also imagined the drain on my bank account. So, I resorted to pulling the bed covers over my head to block out the anxiety, fear, and hopelessness that took up residence in my consciousness.

Eventually, I went to my family doctor, who prescribed me an antidepressant. Soon after, my friend Paula dropped by and suggested I try EFT—the Emotional Freedom Techniques.

"What's EFT?" I asked her.

"You remember about fifteen years ago when I showed you that Tapping method to lower anxiety?"

At this point, she modeled the technique by tapping on her face and body while nodding with her eyebrows raised. A "Remember me showing you this?" look was on her face.

I shook my head. "Yes, I remember, and hell no, Paula. I don't do those new-age, woo-woo things like you. I might be depressed, but I'm not messed up enough to believe my life will improve by tapping on my face."

Paula responded, "It's not new age; it's based on brain science. And since you're sitting in bed nearly twenty-four hours a day, why not try it?"

Maybe you know someone like me who rolls their eyes anytime someone touts the incredible benefits of yoga, meditation, or other non-Western practices—a person who is unaware of the hard science supporting them.

Possibly I was open to trying EFT because the medication had softened my resistance, or maybe I was so sick and tired of being sick and tired. Regardless of the reason, I listened.

There is a saying that the teacher will show up when the student is ready (or, in my case, too depressed and medicated to argue). Hence, when my friend suggested EFT, I gave it a go.

From Drooling Depression to Anxiety-Free

While isolating myself in bed with nothing better to do, I watched YouTube videos of EFT practitioners Tapping, and I began tapping along with them. I found Tapping videos for stress, anxiety, fear, depression, sadness, and loss. I continued watching and tapping, and something started to shift. It didn't result in an immediate miracle with me suddenly rising out of bed and embracing life with gusto. But I wasn't sleeping or crying all day either. EFT lifted the paralyzing blanket of fear and hopelessness, and I began functioning. I don't recall when I rejoined the living world, but I gradually did. I started experiencing glimpses of my old self and, over time, went off the depression medication.

I improved so quickly that it honestly disturbed me. I thought, *I must be pretty messed up to believe tapping on my face and body was helping me out of my anxiety and depression. When will the bottom fall out?* But, to my surprise, it held. I went from drooling depression to much-needed clarity with a Tap of my fingers. Although I occasionally cried and felt overwhelmed, there was no longer a hopeless fear robbing me of my reason and ability to function.

In fact, I felt immediately better each time I Tapped. I had glimpses of life beyond my bedroom and what I considered the death of my family. The most incredible thing about this journey was that the emotional shift became permanent. Even when facing challenges that involved legitimate and almost universal anxiety, like housing, medical insurance, finances, and career choices, I never again dropped into paralyzing fear and despair. In addition to joy and ease, Tapping created an opening for a bigger version of myself—one who was thriving, not just surviving.

This change of attitude was profound, and I wanted to help others achieve the same transformation. However, I was puzzled. Even though my depression and mind fog had lifted, I had no precise understanding of how to recreate what I had experienced during my hours of Tapping along with videos. How could I effectuate this dramatic, life-changing shift through EFT without knowing what I was doing?

This led me to dive deep into researching the brain and EFT. I took an in-depth, eighteen-month EFT certification course from Carol Look, PhD, an expert in the field. This course included studying EFT for trauma and monthly sessions with EFT expert Marti Murphy to analyze the results of Tapping on my own life challenges. I also attended training with the world-renowned Peta Stapleton, PhD, and EFT experts too numerous to mention. In addition, I attended multiple seminars and courses to understand the brain and how stress, anxiety, and trauma affect its structure and our behavior.

So, let me ask: how desirable would a self-regulation intervention method that helps with anxiety, impulsivity, and trauma—that is quick, easy to learn, and works automatically—be to you or your clients? If this sounds appealing, Tapping may be the tool that you have been seeking.

This Book Is for You: Tapping for Professional and Personal Use

Professional Use. Are you a counselor, therapist, or social worker seeking a somatic, mind-body tool to aid your clients in stress, anxiety, and trauma relief?

Does it seem like there is a revolving door where your clients come to you suffering, seem a bit better when they leave your office, and then return the following session just as bad off as when they arrived last session?

Now imagine being able to help them ease their anxiety and work through their trauma without retraumatizing them. Imagine seeing your clients better able to self-regulate and think more clearly. Imagine them saying "No!" to the abusers who keep beating them down, overcoming the triggers of past trauma that once prohibited them from functioning, and leading healthy, productive lives. Imagine helping them heal and build better lives, even when they're not in your office.

Personal Use. You don't have to be a professional to use Tapping to improve your life. If you're struggling with immense stress, exhaustion, and secondary trauma that threatens your resiliency and leads to burnout—as is very common for those employed in the mental health, education, or other caregiver industries—Tapping can help.

Tapping is for everyone who wants an immediate antidote to stress. It helps you outsmart stress and bring your Thinking Brain back from the emotional fog. The Thinking Brain is where decision-making is based on logic and reflection instead of instantly reacting from emotions and fear.

I call EFT "stress relief at your fingertips" because it involves gently tapping the acupuncture meridian points on your body with your fingertips. Tapping reduces stress and anxiety and grounds a person in the present moment. It has the potential to address trauma and other negative emotions without re-traumatization. It removes barriers to treatment and increases self-awareness. Plus, it is free to self-administer anytime and anywhere.

My Promise to You—You'll Be Tapping in No Time!

Upon completing my training, I launched a business designed to help people manage their stress and emotional challenges with EFT. I worked with individual clients and taught variations of EFT to diverse groups. Since starting my business, my efforts have reached an extensive array of professionals including counselors, therapists, social workers, teachers, nurses, foster parents, caregivers, and their clients. Additionally, I shared my knowledge with students, senior citizens, victims of domestic violence, the general public, and people grappling with addictions.

By teaching this large and diverse population, I quickly discerned that the full EFT protocol (which I will refer to throughout the book as traditional EFT) posed certain drawbacks. It is cumbersome and confusing to learn, duplicate, and teach to others.

Considering this realization, I devised two simplified versions of EFT, drawing from my extensive hours spent training others: Functional Tapping (FT) and Simple Tapping Method (STM). My uncomplicated variations of Tapping were designed to foster ease of comprehension and effortless utilization, whether for personal or professional purposes. Plus, these condensed approaches can be used as foundations and tools for those seeking to learn traditional EFT.

When I use the word Tap with a capital T, I am suggesting that you use any type of Tapping that works for you at the time needed. You can use FT to immediately help reduce anxious feelings, or you can use STM because you're at home and have the time to both address anxiety and help to address what is causing the anxiety. A lowercase t represents the mechanical act of tapping or pressing on your body.

When I was lost and mired in despair, holed up in my bedroom, Tapping led me out of a dark place. I know, without a doubt, that it didn't just change my life—Tapping saved it. I want everyone to experience the calming, grounding, and clarity-boosting benefits Tapping offers without having to hit the lowest depths of despair like I did. I want you to be able to take on any size challenge, from deciding which cell phone to purchase to addressing trauma, with calm clarity and intentionality.

If you want this for your clients and yourself, let's begin. The answer is right at your fingertips. You're just a Tap away from a better day.

Tapping puts the power of choice in your hands.

PART ONE

TAPPING: THE BASICS

CHAPTER 1

What is EFT?

EFT is tapping on acupuncture meridian points while focusing on your thoughts and feelings. It aids your physical and mental health by lowering the stress response.

My friend Kathleen had called to complain again about her interior designer. It had been nine months since she'd ordered a new sofa, and the designer had just informed her that the fabric was discontinued. Kathleen needed to start the entire process again and wait another nine months for a sofa. As soon as her voice rose, I asked her to start Functional Tapping (FT), which is picking one EFT meridian point and continually tapping on it while discussing what is bothering you to help with emotional regulation. Halfway through the story's second telling, she blurted, "What just happened?"

Startled, I asked, "What?"

She laughed and said, "I was hoping to vent a little longer be-cause eighteen months is a long time to wait for a sofa. But my anger is completely diffused."

When my friends call me more than once to vent about the same problem, I ask them to FT while sharing. Just repeating the problem aloud rarely induces change. I call it "complaining without changing." Incessant vent sessions do little to alleviate negative emotions; however, tapping while venting accomplishes a lot.

Science is catching up with what EFT, or Tapping, practitioners and the general wellness community have known for some time: Tapping works! And it works fast to create permanent change. After a few minutes of Kathleen venting her emotions and Tapping, her anger had dissipated to the point of laughter.

The Definition of EFT

There are many ways EFT is defined. The following is the technical definition I use most often. Don't fret if it seems complex. The purpose of this book is to simplify the science, theory, and application of EFT. With my step-by-step method and simplified versions of EFT, which you'll learn about in more detail in Chapter Two, you'll be Tapping more and stressing less in no time.

EFT is an evidence-based intervention incorporating exposure, cognitive-therapy, and somatic-stimulation elements. Research suggests EFT affects the body's stress response in the amygdala and the brain's memory center (hippocampus), and appears to have an immediate calming effect on the stress response. It's also called Tapping because the subject uses their fingertips to gently tap on specific points on their face and upper body. These points are based on the ancient Chinese system of acupuncture.

Clinical trials have shown that tapping on or stimulating acu-puncture points on the body radically reduces the levels of the stress hormone cortisol in the body. It also reduces the emotional impact of traumatic memories while positively influencing gene expression and changing brain pathways.

Psychologist and researcher David Feinstein, PhD, explains that tapping on acupuncture meridian points "interrupts the electromagnetic signal going to the brain."[1]

In simpler terms, EFT is a self-regulation tool that combines talking or focusing on what is causing anxiety or stress in your life while tapping with fingertips on specific body points that contain gateways to natural calming agents. EFT reduces the emotional intensity of past experiences that trigger the stress response in the body, often referred to as "trauma triggers." Or, even more simply put, EFT is a self-regulation technique that stops you from stressing and allows you to think clearly. Even though EFT can be defined simply, the actual protocols and concepts confuse people. (Trying to overcome that confusion is how my simplified EFT processes, the focus of this book, were born.)

How Does EFT Work?

The answer depends on whom you ask. If you ask someone steeped in Eastern philosophies and self-help approaches, they will likely explain it from the perspective of acupuncture and emotional energy blocks. However, with contemporary advancements in neuroscience and brain research technology, we now understand that EFT interacts directly with the brain-body connection.

Trauma is a sensory event.

[1] David Feinstein, "Acupoint Stimulation in Treating Psychological Disorders: Evidence of Efficacy," *Review of General Psychology* 16, no. 2 (2012): 364–380, https://doi.org/10.1037/a0028602.

Leading trauma researchers and psychologists Dr. Stephen Porges, Dr. Bessel van der Kolk, Dr. Peter Levine, Dr. Bruce Perry, and others have revolutionized our knowledge of how we respond to anxiety, fear, and trauma. Understanding how human thoughts and emotions connect at the cellular level has given rise to the popularity of EFT within the counseling, trauma, and psychotherapy communities.

Like other therapies that involve the brain and human behavior, science has clues but no definite answers. Since much is still unknown about the workings of the brain, researchers can only form hypotheses.

A Brief History of EFT

EFT is a variation of a somatic psychotherapy technique called "Thought Field Therapy" (TFT) invented in the 1980s by psychologist Dr. Roger Callahan, who created the method to address emotional problems. One of his clients was business performance coach and Stanford-trained engineer Gary Craig. After completing training with Callahan, Craig used TFT as the basis for his version of the therapy, which he named the "Emotional Freedom Techniques." He began by using his new method with his coaching clients, and then, in the mid-'90s, he introduced EFT to the general public through workshops and the distribution of free EFT materials.

However, the seed of EFT is centuries older, rooted deep in the tradition of acupuncture therapy. It is generally believed that acupuncture originated in ancient China, as the earliest written mention of it appears in *The Yellow Emperor's Classic of Internal Medicine*, dating from about 100 BCE. Focusing on the body's internal energy, called "chi" or "qi," acupuncture seeks to restore the balance of this energy when it becomes misaligned by releasing blocked energy.

This blockage is caused by negative emotions and influences and is considered the root of our emotional and physical ailments.

Practitioners traditionally achieve realignment by inserting thin needles into specific meridian points around the body. (This should not be confused with dry needling, a Western medical practice for treating pain and immobility in the neuromusculoskeletal system.)

Shifting Away from Panic

Like acupuncture, EFT deals closely with the meridians. However, EFT utilizes tapping, rubbing, or similar actions on the meridians to break up these negative energy roadblocks, which we call "emotional disturbances." EFT founder Gary Craig explains it through an energy psychology perspective, saying a disruption of the body's energy system is caused by negative emotions.[2] These roadblocks are the catalysts driving one's unwanted or out-of-balance behaviors.

Imagine your body as a communication highway that continually sends signals from all the parts of your body to the brain and back, and your problems as blocks in the road. When you feel a negative emotion due to a problem, or even an anxious thought, a roadblock is formed that impedes the body's usual flow of energy and communication.

These blocks hinder access to the executive prefrontal-cortex brain—your "Thinking Brain"—where decision-making based on logic and reflection occurs. When access to this part of the brain is blocked, the emotional "survival brain," or limbic system, takes the lead. This is often referred to as a "limbic reaction." Later, you will learn more about the limbic system and its influence on your perception of danger. For now, remember that it's called the survival brain for a reason.

The survival brain has the first crack at every situation, determining how you will react. This is true no matter the situation, from dangerous, like discovering a poisonous snake on your doorstep, to innocuous, like deciding which cell phone to purchase. The survival

[2] Gary Craig, *The EFT Manual*, 2nd ed. (Fulton, CA: Energy Psychology Press, 2011).

brain is fear-based and remembers the past to keep you safe in the future. Fear tramples intelligence.

THE BRAIN AND THE STRESS-RESPONSE SYSTEM
Scientists, cognitive neuroscientists, and research psychologists disagree on what to call the various regions of the brain. So, depending on the discipline, you may hear different names for the same structures.
   For the sake of this book, I will refer to stress responses as emanating from the survival brain, or limbic region of the brain. I will refer to logical reasoning and language skills as originating from the prefrontal executive-brain areas, what I call the "Thinking Brain."

When we experience anxiety, the road to the clear-thinking part of the brain becomes blocked. Decision-making detours to the survival brain in hopes of finding logical guidance. Good luck with that plan! Going to the emotional brain for logic is like asking a toddler to give you directions: it isn't happening.

EFT allows you to press pause and reflect, connect, and reframe to see things differently.

Simply put, the human body is electrical. Specialized cells conduct electrical currents, which are required for the nervous system to send signals (communicate) throughout the body and the brain, making it possible for humans to move, think, and feel.

EFT works within our body's electrical system. The panic signal is interrupted when we tap on specific acupuncture meridian points, bringing the logical Thinking Brain back online. The foundation of EFT is this shift from panic to analytical processing. It is a shift from reacting to responding.

BEYOND ACUPUNCTURE: THE SCIENCE OF EFT

Above, I explained the theory of EFT from the perspective of acupuncture and the field of energy psychology. Due to contemporary advancements in neuroscience and our understanding of the brain's functions, we now understand that EFT interacts directly with the brain to help manage stress and anxiety by interrupting electrical signals in our nervous system.

Clinical trials demonstrate that tapping on or stimulating acupuncture points on the body can change DNA expression, radically reducing cortisol (the stress hormone) and even changing brain pathways.

Amygdala: The Gatekeeper of Emotion

Our brain has a threat-detection system, and the amygdalae are in charge. The amygdalae are two small, almond-shaped sections of the brain that are part of the limbic system, commonly referred to by the singular "amygdala." The amygdala is primarily associated with regulating emotions. It plays a prominent role in influencing behavior and is best known for recognizing and processing fear. Even though our understanding of the function of the amygdala is still evolving, it's thought to initiate the "fight-or-flight" response.

The amygdala's job is to keep you alive by recalling past threats. This sounds helpful, but sometimes, it cannot differentiate real dangers from basic stress and anxiety. No matter the source of the perceived threat, the amygdala redirects you away from evaluating with logic and reason and drags you into fear-based reactions.

Your amygdala is always managing risks. Imagine you're at home and the smoke alarm begins blaring. Panic hits, but most of us don't bolt out of the house whenever we hear an alarm. We pause to think and assess the situation. Is the house really on fire, or is the alarm going off because your dinner is burning? The amygdala is the body's smoke alarm. Tapping interrupts the anxiety signal going to your amygdala so you can bring your Thinking Brain back online and assess the situation instead of instantly reacting from an emotional place. Metaphorically, Tapping removes the batteries from the smoke alarm. Once the alarm is no longer blaring, we can stop and think.

Once stress is reduced, our other resources, like logic, reasoning, and self-reflection, become available.

☞ Key Concepts

- EFT is a self-regulation tool that combines talking about what is causing anxiety or stress with tapping on acupuncture meridian points in your face and upper body to induce a calming effect.

- EFT reduces the emotional intensity of "trauma triggers," past experiences that activate the stress response in the body.

- Whether you view EFT through the lens of Eastern philosophy and acupuncture or from the perspective of modern science, Tapping works within our body's electrical system.

- With contemporary advancements in neuroscience, we now understand that EFT interacts directly with the brain to help manage stress and anxiety by interrupting electrical signals in the nervous system.

- The amygdala, a group of brain structures associated with emotion, is a component of the limbic system that functions as the body's metaphorical smoke alarm.

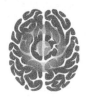

CHAPTER 2

EFT Benefits

Tapping is an antidote to stress.

Stress is universal, impacting the young and old. It can seriously limit cognitive function, leading to unhealthy reactions, intrusive rumination, and narrowed focus.

Anxiety disorders are the most common psychological disorders worldwide. That's not surprising given the fast-paced, high-demanding environment we live in. According to the Anxiety and Depression Association of America (ADAA), one in every eight children has anxiety.[3] In the workforce, we struggle with burnout and try to balance earning a paycheck and enjoying life. Because we are feeling beings, it's not surprising research and health professionals agree that a large percentage of all illness and disease has an emotional component. According to the CDC, 83 percent of

---

[3] "Impact of Anxiety and Depression on Student Academic Progress." IBCCES, April 17, 2020. https://ibcces.org/blog/2019/05/01/impact-anxiety-depression-student-progress/.

all deaths among Americans between the ages of twenty-one and sixty-five are related to lifestyle, which is heavily affected by stress.[4]

Using Tapping

I use Functional Tapping (FT) as a quick fix to lower anxiety for immediate clarity until I have time to fully process my distressing emotions and thoughts with a more in-depth diagnostic Tapping technique, such as EFT or Simple Tapping Method (STM), my simplified form of EFT. The diagnostic capabilities of these more structured Tapping techniques will lower your current anxiety and help you uncover the "why" of the emotional trigger.

You'll learn about both FT and STM in this book. We'll start with FT first, because both STM and EFT utilize the same theory and psychological concepts behind FT. Once you learn this abbreviated and highly effective method, it's just a matter of adding a couple of steps to perform STM and, if you wish, EFT.

Benefits

The benefits of any type of Tapping—FT, STM, or traditional EFT—are numerous.

SELF-REGULATION AND IMMEDIATE GROUNDING

Since I am not handy, when things are broken or damaged, I use duct tape to mend them until I have time to fix them properly. FT is like duct tape. It's an abbreviated form of traditional EFT explicitly used as a self-regulation grounding tool to increase clarity and the ability to function in the moment. Its simplicity makes it straightforward to learn. Once you learn FT, you can incorporate it like any other grounding or self-regulation tool, for personal and professional use.

---

[4] Lucy J. Pearson, "Stress Management for the Health of It," National Ag Safety Database, February 1997, https://nasdonline.org/1445/d001245/stress-management-for-the-health-of-it.html.

Somatic Mind-Body Technique

Tapping is a somatic mind-body technique. This benefit will be explored more throughout the book. For now, I will use this explanation from Licia Sky, somatic educator, bodyworker, and Co-Founder and CEO of The Trauma Research Foundation. She describes emotions and the mind-body connection this way: "Our brains are like the circuit our nervous system goes through, but we feel it in our bodies."

	Traditional EFT	STM	FT
Definition/ Benefits	A self-regulation technique that incorporates exposure, cognitive therapy, and somatic stimulation elements. It alleviates stress and anxiety by tapping or rubbing nine acupuncture meridian points on your face and upper body while focusing on what is bothering you. Traditional EFT aids your physical and mental health by lowering the stress response. It reduces the emotional impact of traumatic memories. It often helps to uncover the core issue causing distress. At times it may elicit strong emotions, so it's not as beneficial to use when you don't have time to work through these emotions.	A simplified version of traditional EFT. I use STM as a foundation to teach traditional EFT.	A simplified version of traditional EFT. I use FT to teach STM and traditional EFT. Used specifically for grounding and self-regulation purposes like you would use a cleansing breath.

	Traditional EFT	STM	FT
How to Perform	**Step One:** Begin tapping on the side of the hand point while stating a phrase called the set-up statement. This statement includes two parts. The first part addresses what you are currently struggling with, and the second part states some form of affirmation. You repeat the set-up-statement three times, all the while tapping on the side of the hand point. **Step Two:** Express or focus on the stressor, and the details surrounding this stressor while continually tapping on the other eight additional EFT meridian points. You repeat this second step numerous times by continuing cycling and tapping on the eight points.	The first step is the same as the second step in traditional EFT. Express or focus on the stressor and the details surrounding this stressor while continually tapping on the other eight additional meridian points. You repeat this numerous times by continuing cycling and tapping on the eight points.	Express what is bothering you while continuing tapping or pressing on one or two traditional EFT meridian points you choose. Typically, a person picks whichever points they feel the most sensations with. Simply Tap, Talk, and Tell the Truth.
When to Use	**Traditonal EFT is a diagnostic and emotional healing tool.** Use traditional EFT to reduce anxiety or reduce influences of painful or traumatic memories by somatically working through them with Tapping.	Same as traditional EFT.	Use to quickly reduce unwanted thoughts and emotions to bring the Thinking Brain back online.

	Traditional EFT	STM	FT
Differences	Requires numerous steps and protocols, so it can be more confusing to learn and not as easily replicated. Continually using the Set-Up Statement can interrupt the flow of the session. When a person is amid strong emotions and visceral, vivid memories, inserting a structured phrase and tapping on it three times can be disruptive and halt the natural flow of the process. There are times when inserting an affirmation before the person has tapped on their anxiety or pain causes them to consciously or subconsciously resist and push back on what is being said, thus creating resistance. With traditional EFT we don't avoid painful thoughts or memories. We lean into and through the pain. So a person needs time to recover from working through strong emotions.	By eliminating the first step, STM is more easily learned and replicated. Without the first step of the traditional EFT protocol, the session can flow naturally and no resistance is created. A person needs time to recover from working through painful memories and emotions.	Since it requires only a couple of meridian points, it is quickly replicated. FT isn't designed to uncover painful memories, so it can be used anytime with no need for processing painful memories or emotions.

Through the rest of the book when I refer to STM, understand that it offers the same benefits as traditional EFT—and visa versa.

CLEAR THINKING

When I was at my low point and full of anxiety, untrue and self-sabotaging statements, such as "I am not enough," "Maybe this is my fault," and "This will never get better," paralyzed me and stunted my ability to think clearly and see my options for moving forward. Tapping can remove knee-jerk reactions stemming from the survival brain so I can see things how they are instead of buying into the stories told by the persistent, scared voice in my head.

Responding from a space of clarity keeps me from getting derailed from my life goals.

Suppose my client needs to have a difficult conversation with someone. Even though she knows avoidance creates more pain, she hates and avoids conflict at all costs. Unfortunately, this chronic thought suppression creates a constant feeling of unease in her stomach. It takes her an exorbitant amount of energy to push down intrusive, anxious thoughts all day.

Even though it is exhausting stuffing down unwanted emotions, we don't want a continuous stream of them thrown around the surface of our awareness like beach balls at a Jimmy Buffet concert. With FT, we can allow these emotions to surface so they can be deflated and no longer have power over us. We can enjoy life without constantly having to dodge triggers flying through the air and smacking us in the face at inopportune times.

Some days, when I experience several challenges or am emotionally off balance, overzealous beach balls rise as a critical committee in my head tries to gain more influence over my life. This is when my clarity dissolves. I react rather than respond, and make choices that don't align with my goals or values and are not representative of my best self. I do things I don't want to do or neglect to act when I should.

I sent a group text to my candid and self-reflective friends, and asked them what occurs when they feel a little off, down, or hear their critical inner voice. Responses instantly came back: "I eat junk food," "Overeat," "Snap at people," "Isolate," "Talk poorly about myself," "Binge-watch TV," "Shop."

Tapping helps slow or stop the fast train of self-judgment from taking you to a dark place where negative feedback loops undermine your goals and reduce the quality of your life. With a little bit of FT, clarity can put you back on the track you choose, not the one laid by past adverse events. Then, when you have some time, you can use STM to dive deeper into what's triggering you and why.

FLEXIBLE AND ADAPTABLE

Whether you use FT personally or professionally, you can integrate it into anything you currently do to enhance emotional health, mental health, and personal growth.

For example:

- Use FT to begin meditation if you are having difficulty calming yourself.

- Use FT while journaling.

- Use FT during therapy when you are feeling anxious talking to your therapist.

- Use FT when praying. (It's a one-two punch: it calms you physically, allowing you to feel extra peace during prayer.)

- Use Public Tapping, a discreet way to tap detailed in Chapter Twelve, to calm social anxiety.

NO HARM

Many people have numerous comorbid problems and are on various medications for mental and physical ailments. For this reason, Tapping is an appealing non-pharmaceutical alternative for addressing mental health issues, anxiety, and trauma. (Of course, check with your doctor before changing any medications.)

EASILY ACCESSIBLE

Many people regularly engage in stress-relief techniques, such as meditation, yoga, massage, and bubble baths (not to mention alcohol, drugs, social media, and binge-watching Netflix). However, these tools aren't always accessible, and some are plain harmful and addictive.

Tapping is always accessible.

If you are stressed at work, you probably can't bust out a yoga pose in the cramped shared workspace. Heading to happy hour at 2 p.m. may also be conspicuous. And what are you to do at a family holiday party when the know-it-all relative makes you feel like the Grinch? Instead of turning to the cookie table and eating your emotions, you could do some Public Tapping. Or you could do some private Tapping in the bathroom and come out refreshed with a clear head so you only have one cookie (or three, if they're good) instead of stress-eating a few dozen!

UNIVERSAL

Tapping is appropriate for anyone. It's especially beneficial for specific populations, like addicts and trauma victims. Tapping is universally accessible, like taking a cleansing breath—anyone can do it. It can easily adjust to cultural preferences, and because it is an automatic physiological response, it has no boundaries such as age, culture, or demographics.

I trained mental health workers in Costa Rica through a brilliant translator named Anne, who efficiently communicated my nuanced

English into Spanish, and participants quickly understood. Tapping is entirely viable in any language.

HOLDS UP UNDER SKEPTICISM

Tapping users don't need to believe in the process. It still works. Remember, it's automatic, like flipping a light switch. Skeptics often approach me after a group Tapping session to report their surprise.

THE TAPPING REFLEX

You may ask, as many have, "How can tapping on your body help with anything? It just looks so ridiculous." I equate the automatic response evoked by tapping on meridian points to the automatic reaction of the reflex test doctors perform. The doctor taps your knee with a rubber hammer, and your foot reflexively pops up. The first time you experienced this as a child, you may have been surprised. However, as an adult, you accept it.

The reflex response is an automatic physiological occurrence. You didn't try to raise your leg; it happened naturally and involuntarily. Similarly, tapping on specific acupuncture meridian points disrupts the brain's conditioned response to the negative emotion or event, ultimately leading to emotional relief. You don't try to make this happen. You tap, your anxiety lessens, and you can engage higher levels of thinking.

FREE

Everyone likes a deal. Most bodies come equipped with fingertips free of charge. If you don't have them, you can use anything that resembles a fingertip. In fact, for FT, you don't even need to use your fingers. I often Tap the side of my hand on the car steering wheel at red lights in a method I jokingly call "Steering Wheel Tapping."

EASILY USED IN SCHOOLS

Tapping is an excellent tool for anyone who works with school children. A lot of schools today teach Social Emotional Learning, which provides students with techniques to help themselves self-regulate before stressful events, such as tests. FT is a simple technique that is easy even for Kindergarteners to learn, and it can be used to help them through testing, social anxiety, bullying, stressful home lives, and more.

FT and STM Use by Mental Health Professionals

If you are a mental health professional, you probably have a toolbox filled with your "go-to" techniques and approaches for clients. FT and STM make valuable additions to your toolbox as they can be used both during therapy sessions and after, when the patient is on their own.

FT can be used with any therapy you are currently administering. Whenever you need a grounding modality, have your client start tapping. Have them pick any EFT meridian point and tap while they are talking. It's okay if they are too emotional to speak; they don't need to because Tapping is an automatic physiological response. Remember: you Tap, you calm.

At any point in the session, STM can be used as a diagnostic tool to help discover the "why" behind an anxiety or behavior—limiting retraumatizing your client.

☞ Key Concepts

- Tapping is an antidote to stress.

- FT and the STM are adaptable to any therapy practices.

- Tapping grounds the user and brings the Thinking Brain back online.

- The numerous benefits and advantages of using FT: easy to learn, offers immediate grounding and clear thinking, is highly adaptable, causes no harm, is accessible any time, is always culturally and age-appropriate, is effective even if the person is skeptical of the modality, and is free to use.

CHAPTER 3

How to Perform Functional Tapping (FT)

Tapping, in its simplest form, is an honest dialogue combined with tapping on acupuncture points to lower any stress response and bring calming clarity.

I was blindsided by a divorce after twenty-five years of a good marriage (or at least I thought it was good). I loved my husband and relished our family life with our four children. When the marriage vanished before my eyes, I became incapacitated. I took to my bed and stayed there for far too long. That's where my Functional Tapping (FT) method was born, as an abbreviated version of traditional EFT. FT helped me summon the emotional strength to get out of bed, function, and thrive.

While suffering in bed, I began Tapping along with traditional EFT practitioners on YouTube. However, the technique was confusing and cumbersome. So instead of following the YouTube instructors' directions to tap all nine acupuncture points, I just picked any EFT meridian point and started tapping it repeatedly. Sometimes, I verbalized my feelings while Tapping, and occasionally, I simply Tapped. Frankly, some days that was all I had the strength for.

I used FT like a cleansing breath to become grounded and centered. The practice felt good. So good that whenever I became stressed, I automatically tapped just one or two of the suggested Tapping points while talking about what was bothering me. Eventually, I realized I was using the mechanical aspect of Tapping to diffuse the near-constant thoughts of hopelessness that dominated my mind.

Even once I became officially trained in traditional EFT, I constantly returned to the simplicity of my FT method. That's when I knew I could use FT to help others.

Below is an example of a typical day as I created and used FT to emerge from depression.

"Wow, it's noon. I probably should get out of bed."

I would suddenly be hit with all-consuming traumatic thoughts—my marriage was over and my dreams were destroyed. The hopelessness was overwhelming.

Tap, tap, tap...The calming nature of Tapping created a sufficient sense of relief, enabling a slight shift in both mental and physical states.

Once I got out of bed and headed for the shower, I noticed the bare space on the double bathroom sink where my husband's toothbrush should have been—another slam to the psyche.

"Why bother brushing my teeth and taking a shower? Everything is gone. The toothbrush, family holidays, vacations, and dreams."

Tears, disbelief, and hopelessness would arise, and I would consider climbing back in bed and escaping reality.

Tap, tap, tap...this would allow a bit more forward movement. But before long, a crushing fear would roll over me. How would I support myself? I quit my lucrative job to raise our children so my husband could build his career. Who would hire a fifty-two-year-old woman who hadn't worked in a traditional job for twenty-three years? So, while crying on my knees, I Tapped, vocalizing my fears and begging God to make this all disappear. **Tap, tap, tap.**

Fast forward three months. I was enjoying tea at a friend's house when her husband walked into the room and kissed her on the cheek (trauma trigger). My happy expression cracked. I mustered a fake smile and eked out a cheery "Hello" to her husband as the familiar feeling squeezed my heart. Instead of sobbing, I excused myself and went into the bathroom, where I **tap, tap, tapped.** This use of Tapping was like taking several calming breaths. It allowed me to return to the room and finish my tea, instead of running home to hide under the covers.

Do you see the pattern here? Fearful, self-defeating, and hopeless thoughts followed by Tapping. Over and over again. And bit-by-bit, day-by-day, I improved.

In this scenario, Tapping was not used to bring about instant positive change in my life. I didn't go from "My life sucks" to "I think I will build a successful EFT practice" after a single tap on the correct pressure point. I used Tapping to get unstuck and show up for life. I didn't realize all that Tapping was effectively breaking the destructive thought patterns and trauma connections in my brain. It allowed me to stay whole even when I saw an empty bathroom vanity or visited married friends with intact families.

Even with traditional EFT, as with most therapies, it's rare for all feelings of loss to disappear permanently. Tapping helped me function, but it did not wholly remove the loss I felt from not having an intact family and the dream surrounding it. When I see a family together, I still feel a tiny tinge of loss, but it's not what I call a "limbic reaction" or "limbic pain." It's not so visceral. The sensation is more like when I see a baby. A warm feeling arises. Then I have a reality check and think, *"Babies are cute, but I have NO interest in going back there. I'm fine, thank you very much!"*

While I unknowingly formed a version of FT while working through my divorce and depression, I officially created FT when working with victims of domestic violence, people with addictions, and children. It was successful in two ways: One, they learned to lower their stress. Two, they could immediately perform the technique on their own, anytime and any place.

Here's the kicker: they didn't know or care why it worked. They immediately experienced lowered feelings of anxiety in their bodies, and that's all that mattered to them. They left my sessions feeling less anxious, more hopeful, and empowered.

Olette, a particularly memorable domestic violence victim in one of my group sessions at a women's shelter, sat expressionless as I explained the benefits of FT to the group. Her face was as lifeless as a mannequin.

Before we started Tapping, she informed me she had lupus. Since feeling negative emotions caused her symptoms to flare, she had decided early in her illness that she would not permit herself to feel any feelings. Ever. Olette explained how hard she had worked NOT to feel. She struggled with her decision and so did her family because they never knew how she felt or how to relate to her. She had few friends because her facial expression was unwelcoming to newcomers who didn't know her backstory.

Imagine the heartbreak of this situation. Because Olette couldn't manage stress or negative emotions, she had denied herself the full experience of life, the enjoyment of even simple pleasures. As I explained to the group that Tapping interrupts the anxiety signals in our mind and body, Olette' eyes widened. "This means I can feel again," she said, tears starting welling up. The shelter director where Olette lived called me a week later to say Olette was making remarkable improvement and had requested that I return to work with her.

Olette improved because she was able to use FT on her own after a single ninety-minute group lesson. This immediate ability to use FT is precisely why I created it. Suppose instead that I had attempted to teach traditional EFT, which includes nine acupuncture points, a confusing step called "the Set-Up to Statement," and a side-of-the-hand point called the "Karate Chop Point." This technical process would have stopped Olette in her tracks. With the ease of FT, Olette had the confidence to try Tapping on her own.

Functional Tapping: Easy and Efficient

Once it became clear that my streamlined version of traditional EFT worked quickly and effectively with groups of students, victims of domestic violence, and people with addiction, I reevaluated how I taught Tapping to mental-health professionals for continuing education credits. I realized social workers, counselors, teachers, caretakers, and nurses also want the benefits FT offers—a quick self-regulation method to relieve stress that can be quickly learned and replicated. Once workshop attendees learn FT, they can easily learn STM and traditional EFT.

When teaching FT, I introduce six of the nine points and ask participants to choose only one to three meridian points that feel right for them. The six meridian points, listed in no specific order, are:

1. **Eyebrow.** Touch the space between your eyes where the eyebrow hair meets your skin.

2. **Side of the Eye.** Touch the smile lines on the sides of your eyes.

3. **Under the Eye.** Touch the top of your cheekbone, under your eye.

4. **Under the Nose.** You've got it; it's where the middle of a mustache would be.

5. **Chin.** It's not directly on the chin. Touch the impression between your lower lip and chin.

6. Top of the **Head.** Touch the top of the head.

Tap, Talk, and Tell the Truth (3Ts)

Sometimes I use FT as a quick grounding tool without talking about what bothers me, almost like a person would use a cleansing breath to calm themselves. However, most of the time, it includes using words. When using words, I call this process the 3Ts: you Tap, Talk, and Tell the truth.

It is crucial to tell your truth by acknowledging your honest feelings, *not* what is culturally and socially acceptable. This truth telling is similar to what you would tell a trusted person about your distress. If being honest with yourself is uncomfortable or frightening, please remember that feelings aren't facts and don't represent who you are. They are fluid and only reflect how you currently feel.

Research suggests that suppressing your feelings and thoughts doesn't make you feel better and may even bring the unwanted thoughts back faster.[5]

Here's what FT looks like in practice.

Imagine this scenario: I am busy preparing dinner and notice my neighbor's teenage son has again parked his car in front of my mailbox. I have already spoken to him and his parents about the

---

[5] Ann E. Lambert et al., "Thought Suppression across Time: Change in Frequency and Duration of Thought Recurrence," *Journal of Obsessive-Compulsive and Related Disorders* 3, no. 1 (January 2014): 21–28, https://doi.org/10.1016/j.jocrd.2013.11.004; D. M. Wegner et al., "Paradoxical Effects of Thought Suppression," *Journal of Personality and Social Psychology* 53, no. 1 (1987): 5–13, https://doi.org/10.1037/0022-3514.53.1.5.

matter because the mail carrier will not deliver my mail if the box is blocked. I don't lose it. This isn't a traumatic event, but I can tell you I definitely feel some feelings! This is one of the times I wish I had the natural capacity to let it go and say, "Kids will be kids. I guess I'll have to call my insurance company and all the other bills I sent today to inform them my payment may be late because I have no idea when this teenager will pull his car away and keep it away. Oh well, no biggie, it only affects my credit score."

Alas, I am not that evolved. Thus, if you were to peek into my kitchen, you would observe me Functional Tapping away my strong emotions so they don't stick and I can move on. Plus, FT will help me have a calm conversation again with this teenager about where he parks, not one laced with frustration and anger.

First, I would look at the car and get irritated. Instantly, I would go to the **Side of the Eye** point and start tapping (remember, the only reason I go to this point first is that I like to, not because this point must be first).

Here is what I would say while Tapping, Talking, and Telling the truth:

"I can't believe Drew parked there again."

"I just talked to him about this last week."

"I don't get it!"

"Doesn't he have respect for others?"

At some point, I would move my tapping fingers to the **Under the Eye** point, still tapping and acknowledging how I feel. (I only go to this point next because it feels comfortable. You are free to choose your own next point.)

"Why doesn't his mother enforce this?"

"Now I have to call several billing departments to discuss my potentially late payments."

"I don't have time for this."

At some point, I may drop to the **Under the Nose** point and continue Tapping, Talking, and Telling the truth (the 3Ts). Eventually, when I want to get back to what I was doing before I noticed his car, I would consciously choose to shift my energy away from my honest feelings of frustration to more pleasant ones. I call this shift "Happy Tapping" because I employ positive phrases to encourage positive energy.

"I'm sure I was also irresponsible as a teenager."

I might add a couple of gratitude affirmations like, "I love this neighborhood, and the Vukoviches are lovely neighbors."

Once you've been Tapping regularly, your body will be conditioned to relax and release your negative feelings quickly without the need to consciously move to Happy Tapping.

Please note that I only employ Happy Tapping *after* clients have shared their true feelings. If clients try to push their negative thoughts down, they spring back like dandelions after the rain. How long must a person tap to ease unwanted emotions? How much time do you have? FT is a tool for quick processing, not a therapeutic technique for complex anxiety and trauma. So, take as much time as you need to become peaceful. Once you get the rhythm of the 3Ts, you will find more ease in your days. You'll feel like you have a secret superpower.

If, after FT, you find you can't let something go, it's probably an indication that there is more going on than what is currently frustrating you. To uncover what this is or the reason for your resistance to letting it go, you can explore the problem with STM.

Functional Tapping

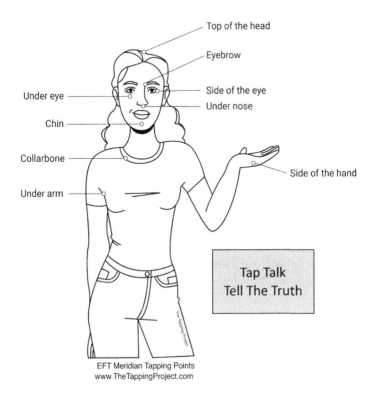

Top of the head

Eyebrow

Under eye

Side of the eye
Under nose

Chin

Collarbone

Side of the hand

Under arm

Tap Talk
Tell The Truth

EFT Meridian Tapping Points
www.TheTappingProject.com

1. Feel It -- Begin Tapping at any EFT point. While tapping, move through a couple of your favorite Tapping points while stating audibly or inaudibly what your frustration or dilemma is, including your emotions. If you desire, you can indicate where you feel the sensations in your body. Feel what you are saying. Tap, Talk, Tell the Truth. The goal is to resolve or become less charged and more neutral to the dilemma.

2. Dump It -- End your Tapping session on positive emotions by dumping the negative words and shift (pivot) to affirmations: "I give a voice to this emotion," "I honor my feelings," "I profoundly love and accept all of me;" "I choose to be calm and peaceful."

For Tapping Videos, Search YouTube: Tijana Coso
*Duplication is permitted with attribution given to Tijana Coso
©Feb 2023 Tijana Coso   Tap@thetappingproject.com
www.thetappingproject.com

☞ Key Concepts

- FT is an abbreviated version of traditional EFT that uses fewer tapping points.

- FT aids in client replication.

- FT includes the 3Ts: Tapping, Talking, and Telling the truth.

- FT can be used without talking. Simply use it like you would use a cleansing or grounding breath.

- You can use Happy Tapping to shift to positive feelings.

- There is no set amount of time to FT to lower an unwanted thought or emotion. How long you Tap is dependent on how long it takes for you to feel calmer.

- If FT doesn't alleviate your unease, use STM to dig deeper and uncover the more complex and deeply rooted triggers.

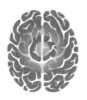

CHAPTER 4

Stress, Anxiety, and How Tapping Can Help

Stress influences our thoughts, behaviors, and the ease with which we navigate life. Because our stress level and mindset frame how we see the world, they also direct how we deal with it.

When I was going through my divorce, I had two car accidents in three months. In one of them, I totaled my car. Before that, I was accident-free for over thirty years.

I also lost my dog, Cody. Well, I thought I did. It was winter, and I decided to take him to the park for a long hike. But when I went to get him, I couldn't find him anywhere in the house. I thought someone had entered my house and stolen my dog. You might wonder why and how someone would enter a home to kidnap a ninety-five-pound, eleven-year-old yellow Labrador.

That question never entered my mind because I was living with chronic anxiety.

Eventually, I found him. He was asleep in my (not running) car in the garage, waiting to go to the park. I had forgotten I had already put him in there.

How Stress and Anxiety Work

We all have had thoughts that seem to eat us up inside. Sometimes, we ruminate so much about them that they take over our entire thought process, building mountains out of molehills. They distract us from what we should be doing. Think of a time when something bothered you so much that, no matter how you tried to distract yourself, the anxiety-inducing thoughts kept creeping in. These joy-stealers ruin your day and can wreak havoc on your car insurance rates and sanity.

Stress and suffering are part of the human condition. According to the World Health Organization, stress is a significant problem in our world, affecting people's physical and mental health.[6] The American Psychological Association reports that stress is a national mental health crisis.[7]

Stress, along with anxiety, activates a reaction often called the "fight-or-flight response." This can be induced by real or imagined threats. Both stress and anxiety have similar effects on your body, physiologically and emotionally.

Often, the anxiety-causing thoughts in our head aren't based on fact and logic. When you prophesize about something in the

---

[6] International Labour Organization and World Health Organization, "Psychosocial Factors at Work: Recognition and Control," *Occupational Safety and Health Series* no. 56, report presented at Joint ILO/WHO Committee on Occupational Health, Ninth Session, Geneva, Switzerland, 18–24 December 1984, https://ilo.primo.exlibrisgroup.com/permalink/41ILO_INST/1jaulmn/alma992480113402676.

[7] American Psychological Association, "Stress in America 2020 Survey Signals a Growing National Mental Health Crisis," press release, October 20, 2020, https://www.apa.org/news/press/releases/2020/10/stress-mental-health-crisis.

future that you believe will happen, it can cause anxiety. These self-created stories influence our behaviors. An example might be when you "absolutely know" you will make a fool of yourself during a presentation at work. Or you "know" the mom group doesn't like you or your child. Or you "know" everyone notices your shirt is tight because you gained ten pounds.

Anxiety is like time-traveling to the past or future instead of living in the present. In other words, you are not interacting with the current reality but with a fantasy you are imagining. Tapping can change that.

Imagine that you experienced a devastating car accident twenty years ago at an intersection close to your grandmother's house. As a result, you faced considerable medical expenses and suffered a loss of income. Even now, you may still feel anxious whenever you pass through that intersection. For instance, the day before you plan to visit your grandmother, your mind might wander into worrisome thoughts like, "What if something like that could happen again?"

Eventually, rationality kicks in, and you reassure yourself, saying, "No, that's unlikely to happen again. I was an inexperienced driver back then." You try to dismiss the thought and push it down. Regrettably, as you prepare for bed, it refuses to stay suppressed. It's akin to trying to hold a beach ball underwater, only to have it resurface in your consciousness. It keeps replaying in your mind, repeatedly interrupting your attempts to fall asleep. Consequently, a restful night's sleep becomes elusive!

Fear gains control as this fabricated scenario of a dreadful accident flashes through your mind. You find yourself trapped in a whirlwind of stress-induced, irrational thoughts that hinder clear thinking and impede the ability to make sound, well-balanced decisions.

What if I get in a car accident again and have to go through another nine months of physical therapy?

That will cause me to miss work again.

I won't be able to pay my bills and will have to move out of the house I just bought.

Honestly, I don't know if I should have purchased this house in the first place.

What if I become depressed and gain thirty pounds like last time because I couldn't work out?

Oh, no! I threw away all my fat clothes when I moved into this new house!

(And it goes on and on...)

These tumbling thoughts are not consciously generated. They creep in under the radar, flying through your mind while doing the dishes, driving, preparing a work report, or staring off into space. They distract you from your present moment and can adversely misdirect your future decisions.

Tapping helps you to behave in the ways you consciously choose to live.

It's best not to respond from a place of imagined threat but to shift your decision to balanced, whole-brain thinking. This sweet spot is called "homeostasis." Balanced thinking uses your whole brain and does not rely solely on the over-protection safety signals from your survival brain or the logic of your Thinking Brain.

Tapping helps the body adjust and maintain balance and equilibrium despite sensory inputs.

The Biology of Decision-Making

To understand this shifting process, let's look at a simplified explanation of the biology of decision-making and the brain-body connections, which are deeply rooted in the evolution of human behavior.

Put your hand on your forehead. This is approximately where your Thinking Brain is located. This is where you make decisions based on logic, facts, analysis, and reasoning. These decisions are full of blood. That may sound a little disgusting, but loosely speaking, if there is less blood under the palm of your hand in those prefrontal lobes, your decision-making will shift to your survival brain where thoughts and behaviors arise out of fear. Stress causes blood to leave this area and travel to the larger muscle groups in your arms and legs so you can "fight or flee."

The problem is that we aren't usually fighting a real person or fleeing legitimate danger. We're battling with the destructive thoughts in our heads. Once triggered, our primal threat-detection system immediately sends blood from our prefrontal lobes to our extremities, leaving our frontal lobes too drained to make mature, logical decisions.

When you sense a threat (real or perceived), your alarm system (limbic region) automatically energizes the body, moving blood in preparation for fight or flight. Your heart pounds. Your breathing quickens. Your body immediately and efficiently shuts down every non-essential system, preparing you to face a threat or run to safety. Speedy, instinctual reactions triggered by the limbic brain region ensure your survival as opposed to the slower, logical processing of your prefrontal lobe, or Thinking Brain.

This primitive response can be traced back to the days when humans faced threats from predators like lions, tigers, and bears—"Oh my!" Imagine a lion chasing you: what would you do? You wouldn't initiate your prefrontal lobe, thinking and pondering on the best option forward.

In this scenario, the immediate reaction makes perfect sense. Right? "Survival is key; long live me!" The reality is that most of us don't have man-eating animals threatening our survival, yet we react all day long as if we were about to become something's lunch.

Typically, anxiety born from first-world problems is unrelated to survival concerns. It often grows from non-life-threatening thoughts and messages. *How am I going to get all this paperwork done? Should I go back to school? Which café drive-thru will be the fastest at this time of day? Why do I have so many TV subscriptions? Do we need Disney+?*

Imagine the ability to control your emotions and reactions. To be able to respond, not react, when triggered by a memory, hurtful comment, or even a long line at Starbucks. Life would become much more enjoyable if we could interact with the world from a place of embodied calm.

Tapping helps you notice alternative perspectives to the present problem.

Panic-to-Please Alarm

Panicking is understandable when you think you've lost your cell phone, wallet, or keys (or are being chased by a lion). However, automatically and indiscriminately sounding the alarm can cause unnecessary stress and negative thinking to take over.

We are what we have experienced through life. Just as each of us has individual alarms set on our phones to help navigate our days, our bodies have their own alarms installed, causing us to react in ways directly related to our past adverse experiences. We create these preference systems in our minds and use their unchecked guidance to navigate life. You have probably heard someone say, "I don't know what happened to me. I just lost my head." Well, once the panic alarms were sounded, they did lose the front part of their head. Their thinking was hijacked!

I have trained thousands of social workers, counselors, and teachers, and I find that many within these fields are hardwired to go to extraordinary lengths to please people. Their desire to help is part of their identities, which is likely why they became a helping professional.

With this innate desire to help often comes an automatically installed panic-to-please alarm that keeps them from saying no or setting boundaries with friends, peers, loved ones, and, sometimes, clients. To them, saying no does not align with their values and identity. It unconsciously triggers anxiety and gives rise to the panic-to-please alarm.

However, while Tapping with people on their reluctance to set boundaries or say no to a request, I have discovered other reasons for the panic-to-please response that have nothing to do with values and identity.

After engaging in Tapping, individuals gradually acknowledge hidden truths, which frequently surprise them. They might learn they resist setting boundaries for fear of being judged selfish, disappointing or hurting others, causing conflict, or being abandoned. Others openly admit what they already knew: being excessively helpful may not always be beneficial for all parties involved and can, in fact, create problems. Nevertheless, they confess that withholding assistance can be more unbearable than the potential repercussions of being overly helpful. This sentiment holds particularly true in the context of family members.

Tapping also facilitates the emergence of a paradoxical emotion: resentment.

A social worker from a large family reluctantly shared the following: "I hate to admit that sometimes I resent my family and friends for taking advantage of me, even though it's not their fault that I can't say no."

With the self-reflection from Tapping, many wish they could install an alarm signaling that their decision-making is defaulting to an unhealthy "yes" behavior. *Alert! Alert! You are defaulting to your automatic response. You can say no. I repeat: no one will die if you say no.*

My mother always said that people don't die from disappointment. Of course, she's right. If only we could avoid the suffering we experience when we have to be the person doing the disappointing.

> *Tapping allows you to feel the pain*
> *and remain true to yourself.*

Tapping Tip for Boundary Setting: FT will help re-engage the Thinking Brain. With this newfound clarity, individuals may uncover alternative solutions to their dilemmas. They may also cultivate the courage to prioritize their own well-being, even if it means disappointing others, while simultaneously letting go of any lingering guilt associated with it. Then, using STM, you can dive deeper to discover the origin of your panic-to-please alarm and remove its batteries once and for all.

☞ Key Concepts

- Stress and anxiety can be based on real or imagined threats.

- Stress automatically initiates a biological and physiological response.

- The stress response is sometimes called the "threat-detection system."

- The threat-detection system initiates from the limbic system (emotional brain), an area of the brain that helps us form and store long-term memories associated with past emotional events. It influences our current perception of present danger.

- We create habits based on past threats and use their unchecked guidance to navigate life.

- Once stressed, our logical, adult thinking is hijacked and goes offline. We figuratively lose our heads.

- Tapping helps with boundary setting, and STM helps uncover the reasons for a reluctance to set boundaries.

- Tapping helps you press pause, allowing time for you to consider saying no.

CHAPTER 5

Using STM and Traditional EFT to Uncover and Remove Barriers from the Past

"Between stimulus and response there is a space.
In that space is our power to choose our response.
In our response lies our growth and our freedom."
—Stephen Covey

You may be wondering why you're reading all this talk about the origins of stress if this book is supposed to be about relieving stress, not initiating it. Your emotional brain influences the choices you make all day long. Consequently, this brain area's flawed, pre-programmed decisions affect how you interact with clients, students, peers, family, and others. You may think you are in control, but you're not. Our thoughts are like a gif on an infinite loop. They are unresolved emotional conflicts that determine our present and future. These messages, formulated without our consent, often stem from everyday childhood stress, anxiety, and adverse childhood events. They create panic signals that aren't based on actual threats. Yet their childlike perspective influences adult behavior and develops into unhealthy, habitual coping strategies.

The Simple Tapping Method (STM) as a Diagnostic and Healing Tool

FT, STM, and traditional EFT all have numerous benefits. However, FT is explicitly used for quick grounding and to aid in balanced thinking. If there isn't an underlying negative memory or childhood experience causing a person's distress, then using FT for anxiety can offer relief. Yet, sometimes it doesn't provide permanent results, and you may wonder why not. *Why am I still anxious? Why can't I get over this? Why don't I seek a new job? Why don't I set a boundary with my brother? Why do I continue to_____?*

What I call the Simple Tapping Method (STM) adds more structure to FT. Using STM, therapists can assist clients in quickly uncovering the core issue, possibly saving months of unnecessary exploration, and putting the client in the fast lane to improvement or recovery.

You can also use STM on yourself. Let's say you have a problem that confuses you; for example, a know-it-all at work drives you bonkers, and you want to know why. You can unravel this mystery by employing STM's diagnostic methods to bring clarity, reflection, and connection, then identify and resolve the core issue creating this trigger.

The issue is not always obvious and usually hidden beneath the story you or your client is willing to say out loud. For example, my client Rose Marie was anxious about which computer to buy. She claimed she was just confused about which model to purchase. The operative word here is "claimed." Using STM, we discovered she was not confused at all. She knew precisely which computer she wanted and had the funds to purchase it. Her so-called confusion and subsequent procrastination stemmed from a question of worthiness. Did she deserve a new computer even though her current one wasn't broken?

The belief that she might not be worthy stemmed from her childhood. Through STM, we also discovered that feeling unworthy was a pervasive theme in her life. She wasn't worthy of a computer and other necessary self-care, such as healthy boundaries and a loving partner. This belief was subconscious and, therefore, unknown to her. Not until we used STM could she access this deeply buried information. After the session, she was able to purchase the computer she wanted anxiety-free and continued using STM to learn more about her feelings of unworthiness.

Most people contact me to help them address stress and anxiety, as Rose Marie did when she experienced anxiety and confusion around purchasing a computer. Using STM, we typically discover a past adverse experience as the underlying cause of their distress. These experiences can be small or big traumas perpetuating unwanted emotions and unease.

A seventy-seven-year-old woman named Suzanne, who had been married for over fifty years, needed help with anxiety surrounding her hoarding. She would not toss anything away until she read every word on the packaging. She kept things that most people almost immediately pitched, such as empty cereal boxes, bottles of shampoo, and the packaging from kitchen utensils, like a measuring cup. Suzanne wouldn't throw any of these away because she feared she would throw out something valuable. She explained that she and her husband might have to move to the basement because the upstairs didn't have much available space left.

Suzanne wanted me to help her lower the anxiety she felt when she attempted to throw things away. She did not contact me to help her understand the reason for her hoarding or to hopefully resolve the problem. However, that is precisely what happens when you employ STM.

The calming response of Tapping allowed Suzanne to feel safe enough to tolerate the pain of awareness. From this state, introspective connections were made, and she was able to verbalize a fifty-eight-year-old trauma that was the unconscious catalyst for her hoarding.

When Suzanne was nineteen years old, she had an abortion, and at the time, she didn't realize how traumatic it was for her. She had no idea this trauma was the cause of her hoarding. In fact, she hadn't thought of the abortion since her late-twenties when her first child was born, which triggered feelings of regret. Even though she had not thought about the abortion in fifty years, hoarding was an unconscious manifestation of her pain.

Here are several examples of surprise connections that were revealed when I used STM with clients:

- Restless leg syndrome. A woman with restless leg syndrome realized it stemmed from feeling trapped in her marriage and wanting to run away.

- Weight loss. A man realized he sabotaged his weight loss because he didn't want to be controlled by loved ones. As a child, he had controlling parents.

- Test taking. A woman realized her emotions surrounding taking an exam for her nursing license stemmed from resentment towards her husband pressuring her to hurry and take her state exam to help get the family out of debt from his gambling.

- Fear of opening a new business. A woman feared losing the friends she had made at her current place of work if she left the company and opened a new business. This unwarranted fear stemmed from a childhood loss.

The grounding nature of Tapping made them feel safe enough to handle introspection and connections.

Introspection

"Knowing yourself is the beginning of all wisdom."
—Aristotle

What about you and your goals, relationships, and values?

Maybe there is hidden anxiety influencing your choices and behaviors. Are you procrastinating returning to school, attending advanced training, or seeking a new job? If you logically know you could succeed, what is holding you back? What is the story or doubt derailing you from committing to your goals? Are you a little soft on boundary setting in your relationships with a client, friend, or loved one? Are you justifying your and their behavior? Is being silent on this matter having integrity and aligning with your values?

Both STM and traditional EFT can help uncover why you continue with these maladaptive patterns that don't serve you. One of the central truths often revealed with STM and traditional EFT is that there is a payoff to every behavior: survival. I know that sounds dramatic because people don't typically die if they love freely, set a boundary, or seek an advanced degree. But that's how the emotional survival brain interprets the situation.

The payoff is usually evading a feeling that we don't want to feel or a thought we don't like to acknowledge. Tapping's sleuthing ability is unique, powerful, and life-changing. It will help you uncover why you have thrown unnecessary barriers into your life. Tapping gives you back your ability to choose your reactions, instead of being forced to follow the decisions made in your youth.

"If you eliminate your fear of failure and drop your tensions about succeeding, you will be yourself. You will be relaxed. You won't be driving with your brakes on." —Anthony de Mello

☞ Key Concepts

- Thoughts and emotions are messages that drive behavior.

- Stress and anxiety operate well below our awareness level and can create panic.

- Panic can block learning and loving, keep us from being fully present, cause us to make choices that don't align with our goals and passions, and create patterns for living.

- People are not often aware of their unconscious stress triggers.

- Negative thoughts based on childhood anxiety and trauma recycle themselves into our minds.

- STM is an especially effective diagnostic tool to discover the origins of these triggers.

- STM helps you to see reality, not the story you are telling yourself.

- STM allows honest self-examination without judgment and with understanding.

CHAPTER 6

Using Tapping to Uncover and Address Traumas Big and Small

"One of the paradoxical and transformative aspects of implicit traumatic memory is that once it is accessed in a resourced way (through the felt sense), it, by its very nature, changes."
—Peter A. Levine

One of the most fascinating things I've discovered while working with clients is the significance of small traumas—I call these "small 't's." A small "t" is a seemingly innocuous event or experience that occurred in your past that you filed away as unimportant. However, when triggered, your body remembers it as significant and alerts you to "danger."

It is essential to understand that these experiences, whether one-time or ongoing, are minor compared to events generated from developmental trauma or other severe trauma. A small "t" has nothing to do with a life-threatening situation. Often, it is caused by an interpretation of an experience from a child's viewpoint. This small "t" leads to a lifetime of anxiety and habitual patterns. I call them small "t"s because even though they are less evident and grave in scope, they can have a surprisingly constrictive or destructive impact on your life.

STM and traditional EFT are effective ways to uncover small "t"s that create anxiety and adversely influence behaviors. When I was a career- and personal-development coach using EFT, I found small "t"s were the causes of most of the dilemmas people were experiencing. What made these discoveries fascinating was that the person never, and I mean *never*, realized these small "t"*s* were directly related to their current struggles until they tried Tapping.

Here are some examples where Tapping helped discover small "t" traumas.

Perfectionism. "I never connected my need to always look perfect to growing up in a disgustingly dirty household packed with stuff resulting from my mother's hoarding problem. I never had friends over because I was embarrassed. I thought if I looked perfect, no one would know our dirty family secret."

Anxiety. "My mother had a chronic illness throughout my childhood, so we children always had to be quiet. Do you realize how hard that is? We were punished if we displayed any emotion, whether joy or anger. I can now see why I learned to stuff all my feelings deep down and never express them. We weren't permitted to feel. And no wonder I let my children go a little crazy in the house. I don't want them to stuff things down like I did."

Financial anxiety. "I didn't realize that my tendency to be over-generous may have stemmed from growing up having less money than my friends. During my elementary school years in the fifties, it was customary for students to give Christmas presents to their teachers. On the last day of school before the holiday break, the teacher would open the gifts in front of the class. I always felt deeply embarrassed as I watched my classmates' beautiful gifts being opened, knowing that mine wouldn't compare. This annual humiliation became something I started dreading as early as Thanksgiving.

In one particularly distressing year, I was so ashamed of the gift I was supposed to give the teacher that I threw it away. Instead, I resorted to taking something from my aunt's house to present as a substitute gift. Not only did I feel guilty for discarding the gift my mother had purchased, but I also had to lie to her when she asked if the teacher liked what we had given her. On top of that, I feared being discovered as a thief."

A magician uses a distraction or misdirection to perform a magic trick. Only when they reveal the slight of hand do you understand how you were fooled. At least with a magic trick, you know a deception is occurring. The insidious nature of a small "t" is that you are the one pulling the wool over your own eyes—without realizing it.

Lynn's Story

Lynn contacted me about what she called her "career stall." She and her new husband had moved to another state, delaying her return to college to finish her degree. Through Tapping, we discovered that she had a small "t."

Back when she was six, Lynn moved to a new town. When asked about the experience, Lynn casually stated, "Even though the experience was not positive, it wasn't traumatic or anything like that. Children change schools all the time. Plus, that was way back in my past."

With Tapping, we discovered that Lynn's transfer to a new school district may not have been a significant trauma, but it was a small "t."

Her childhood move fifteen years earlier triggered her present anxiety about starting at a new college. It didn't make any difference that she was now an adult with grown-up capabilities. In this instance, her courage to register for classes had less to do with her current ability and more with her fear of being the new kid in school.

Maybe, like Lynn, your protective emotional brain is triggered when you think of applying for a position, changing companies, or starting your own business. Even though logically you know you have the skills required for the move, this small "t" is a secret dream stealer, instructing you to play it safe and remain in your current position. When in a tug of war between what to do and what not to do, fear-based emotional decisions win over logic nearly every time.

Small "t" adverse experiences can stealthily cause strife and create the lens through which we view our lives. They are silent dream killers and often block us from our full potential, beckoning us to play it safe and stay small.

Abraham Maslow is often quoted as saying, "You will either step forward into growth, or you will step backward into safety."

When Tapping with clients, I use safety as a litmus test, examining every behavior through the safety and survival instinct. This goes back to the premise that your body's cells are the servants of your mind, and there is a payoff to all behavior. So if it isn't safe to think, feel, or see something, your survival brain directs your behavior accordingly.

It relies on your Thinking Brain to make up a story using false logic to support and legitimize your actions and behaviors because we are sense-making beings. Therefore, we must justify our choices even if they fly directly against what we claim we want or know is true.

When people discover that something from their childhood is influencing their current behaviors, like the story with Lynn, they are shocked and annoyed. I often hear comments like, "Are you kidding me? What happened to me in third grade is causing me to avoid becoming a supervisor?"

I tell my clients to embrace the wisdom gleaned from the small "t" because it's good to know that we aren't just crazy or lazy, and neither is our behavior. We have a small "t" that wields considerable power, and now we can use traditional EFT or STM to tame the small "t" and allow healthy behaviors to emerge that serve us.

Implicit Bias and My Small "t"s

Small "t"s hold you prisoner to your past.

I recently discovered that I have an implicit bias against skinny, tall women with broader shoulders and longer limbs than mine. (FYI, anyone over five foot two is tall to me.) I discovered my peculiar prejudice while working as a co-leader for a young women's mentorship program. My co-leader was a woman I'll call Anaz, whom I had not previously met.

At our first meeting, I liked her. I experienced one of those instant chemistry connections with her and was looking forward to working together. I told my friends how excited I was to partner with a dynamic woman who also had a passion for helping young people. I was thrilled to partner with her on this new adventure—until I worked alongside her. Then, my small "t" became triggered, and my positive energy regarding her evaporated.

I felt the young participants listened to Anaz's comments and thoughts more than mine (please note: whenever someone says "felt," think: the emotional brain). They seemed to like her more. I didn't understand why they would, because I didn't believe she offered any wiser information than I did. (Do I sound like a jealous high schooler?)

Unfortunately, this mentoring experience ignited insecurity within me. It triggered my "less than" button. Equally unfortunate is that it spread into my interactions with Anaz. In fact, after one of the trainings, I made a few remarks to her that bordered on snarky.

Driving home, I realized how unprofessional my behavior had been. However, I didn't think about *why* I acted this way. Since this childish behavior did not align with my values, I was sorely embarrassed and decided I needed to make some kind of amends to Anaz.

Yet, I procrastinated apologizing, because I feared being vulnerable. Remember something I've mentioned several times: there is a payoff to all behavior. My emotional brain decided that exposing my unprofessionalism to her wasn't safe. So, it enlisted my Thinking Brain to justify my behavior and create a plan that wouldn't expose my weakness. Because of the fear of vulnerability, I didn't step forward into growth but retreated to safety.

Here are the excuses I rationalized for not apologizing to Anaz for my unprofessional behavior:

OPTION 1: MY OVERCOMPENSATION BEHAVIOR
Maybe there is a choice other than directly apologizing to her for my unprofessional behavior. I know what I could do instead! I could buy her a small gift for her upcoming birthday. Nothing big. This way, I can hopefully relieve my guilt for being a bit snappy. (Doesn't

snappy sound better than rude? I am such a master storyteller, plus I was protecting myself from being vulnerable. Dang, I'm good!)

OPTION 2: AVOIDING MY FEELINGS

Or maybe I'm a little stressed and need to treat myself to a shopping spree. I do have a $5-off coupon for my favorite shoe store that expires this month.

(Good ol' Suppress and Distract works every time!)

OPTION #3: TIME TO FLEE JUSTIFICATION

On the other hand, maybe this unease has nothing to do with distress at interacting with Anaz. Possibly it's a sign that this group mentoring thing is not the right fit for me. Maybe I should quit and move to another project. I'm too busy anyway. (Fight, flight … I think I will flee!)

Since I was unhappy with myself, I Tapped when I got home. Sure enough, I discovered I had a small "t" from a high school gymnastics event that triggered my reactions. Like my disbelieving clients, I slapped a hand on my forehead and lamented, "Are you kidding me? Please say it ain't so!" A high school event that wasn't abuse, rape, bullying, or a natural disaster still affected me as a fifty-year-old.

I was on my high school gymnastics team. Before competing at a meet and after warmups, we were required to walk past the judge's table. I stood directly next to my friend, a blond high school version of Anaz. As she stood before one of the male judges, he told her he had seen her perform a walkover during the warmup. He then stated, with an admiring smile and twinkling eyes, "If I could, I would give you extra points because your legs made beautiful, long, straight lines when you practiced your walkover." She smiled, nodded, and moved on. Then I stepped in front of him.

He blandly took in all five feet one inch of me and immediately looked down at his papers without comment. I awkwardly smirked and skulked on. As an adult, I understand his behavior was inappropriate. But back then, his rebuff was a slap to my ego, and I felt less than.

I should have held this slight against the judge, but it was probably one of the first wedges I inserted in the friendship between my blonde friend and myself. What's genuinely unfair is that it's not her fault that I wasn't tall, thin, or blonde.

You Live Your Unconscious Beliefs

The above story with Anaz is an example of how my insecurities influenced my goals and values. I had a passion for helping young people, I liked this group, and I don't like being rude.

If I hadn't Tapped on my unease, I would have quit the group, missing out on the opportunity to help others. I would have been unconsciously ashamed of my behavior, causing me to avoid Anaz. I would also have had to dodge my friends' inquiries about why I quit the mentorship program that I was so excited about joining.

Actually, that isn't accurate. I wouldn't have to avoid the inquiry from my friends, because I'm sure my frontal-lobe reasoning machine would have jumped in to rescue me with all sorts of justifications and rationalizations as to why I must quit. My primitive survival brain is a master storyteller, after all.

It was too far of a drive.

I don't have the time.

It's not what I expected.

Maybe I should try something else. Perhaps I should volunteer again at the hospital and deliver papers and plasma. The hospital staff were extremely grateful!

When the limbic brain panics, the logical brain lies.

Your "t"s, My "t"s: All "t"s Can Hurt

Without knowing it, you may have pushed someone's button stemming from a small "t." A good indicator of this is if their reaction seems inappropriate. An oversized reaction can send you reeling and feeling utterly confused, wondering what you did to cause them to react the way they did. I have found that when people over- or under-react, it is often due to a safety mechanism developed long ago because of a small "t."

☞ Key Concepts

- Tapping is an all-purpose tool.

- You can use FT to feel the fear and change your behavior. You can also use FT to handle the discomfort you experience from another person's behavior.

- Traditional EFT and STM can be used as diagnostic tools to discover what experiences are causing anxiety—to discover the "why."

- A small "t" is a seemingly innocuous event or experience that occurred in our past, which we filed away as unimportant. However, our body remembers its significance and will alert us to danger when it's triggered.

- We can be aware of our small "t"s, or they can operate well below our awareness. Either way, they influence our behavior.

- Pay attention to contradictions between values, goals, and behaviors. They can tell you where a small "t" is hiding.

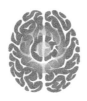

CHAPTER 7

Simple Tapping Method (STM) and Traditional EFT

*Tapping helps you treat
what your clients can't verbalize.*

I teach STM under the framework of Label It, Feel It, Dump It (LFD), outlined in the STM document below. I use this document during the discovery process when gathering information to guide the Tapping session. I don't give clients the document. I fill it out myself.

Simple Tapping Method: Label It, Feel It, Dump It (LFD)

The document below is used with STM, not traditional EFT, so it doesn't include the Set-up Statement and Side of the Hand tapping point.

Let's Break It Down

STM is not a passive technique. It is a problem-resolution intervention method. It is designed to move a person from Feeling A (unwanted) to Feeling B (wanted), which typically is the opposite of Feeling A. To do so, we first need to determine what Feeling A is.

When working with clients, I always have them FT while they share their problem with me since it calms the body and aids clarity. I'll say, "Pauline, please pick one of the FT points and tap while you share your concerns."

USING THE STM DOCUMENT

Examples of client scenarios:

1. Label It—Describe the dilemma.

Here are some examples of client scenarios:

- My (adult) son is drinking again.
- My husband doesn't make time for the family.
- My wife has a spending problem.
- My mother is overly critical.

If you notice, none of these client statements mention an emotion. We will address identifying an emotion in Step 3.

2. Label It—The Content.

Like any therapy session, you should ask them for particulars about their presenting problem. "While tapping, tell me about your problem." The more specific the details, thoughts, images, or even words that trigger emotions, the better. It can even include trite snippets of he said, she said.

Explain to your clients that they need not worry about sounding too catty, jealous, angry, or whiny. They should share their current thoughts and feelings without social editing.

Example:

Dilemma: "My son is drinking again."

Details: "I know this because his ex-wife has called me. He's drunk, roaming around our small town. He won't return my phone calls. At one point, I gave him a phone with a prepaid card, but I don't even know if he still has it. I don't know where he is living. Friends who have seen him say he looks terrible. He isn't working or paying his wife child support for their children. And we tried to help. We paid for alcohol treatment twice already...(and on and on)...I am just so upset. I cry throughout the day."

3. Label It—The emotion you feel when you think of the struggle noted above.

I liken the discovery of identifying the core feeling or beliefs to the process of Tapping while progressing down a funnel filled with layers of emotions. The top, where the funnel is the widest, is where general emotions, like frustration, anxiety, and overwhelm, live. The bottom is where you'll find the core emotions.

Clients typically start sharing the innocuous, safer, and more socially acceptable words and emotions. Sometimes, they begin with these because they unknowingly have been suppressing their genuine emotions for years and aren't aware of them. They were raised in homes where feelings were not welcome or safe to express, so they could not feel a connection to something deeper. Or they may be numbing themselves with medication to avoid, what I like to call, the icky and sticky.

Whether you are working with a client or yourself, start with what appears to be the essence of the dilemma, as the client presents it, and Tapping will take care of the rest. Once Tapping, more accurate (core) feelings like resentment, hurt, anger, fear, and guilt will surface.

Simple Tapping Method (STM)
Label It – Feel It – Dump It (LFD) System

1. Label It -- Describe the dilemma. What's bothering you? Finish this sentence: I am struggling with _____

2. Label It -- The content. Write down details and thoughts about the dilemma/stressor. The more specific, the better. Or finish the sentence: I'm struggling with _____(above dilemma) because_____(the details as you see them).

3. Label It -- The emotion you feel when you think of the above struggle. You can pick a general emotion; however, for STM to be most effective, you must uncover a core emotion. If you can't identify a core emotion, it should arise after some Tapping. "When I think of_____(dilemma), I feel___(emotion)."
- Examples of general emotions: upset, frustrated, overwhelmed, anxious, stressed, controlled, sad, unheard.
- Examples of core emotions: anger, fear, resentment, unloved, hurt, abandoned, shame.

4. Feel It -- Create Your Target Statement. Combine dilemma/stressor, emotion and body part: chest, heart, stomach.
Example: "When I think of it_____(above stressor), I feel _____ (emotion). And I feel this ____(emotion) in my _____ (body part)."

5. SUD Score (number) -- Rate the intensity of the emotion you feel from one to ten, with ten having the most charge. Use this as a baseline SUD score, and then, following several Tapping Rounds, compare the current SUD (number) to the initial SUD. A Tapping round is one pass through the Tapping points. Example of a SUD score (intensity number): "My anxiety regarding the new job is an eight."

6. Feel It -- Begin Tapping at any EFT point. While tapping, move through the points while reading the above details, including the emotion and where you feel the sensations in your body. Feel what you are saying. Tap, Talk, Tell the Truth. After several Tapping Rounds, re-state your Target Statement and give it a SUD score. Compare the current SUD to your baseline SUD score. The goal is to resolve or become less charged and more neutral to the dilemma. If new aspects and emotions arise, use the STM to address these.

7. Dump It -- End your Tapping session on positive emotions by dumping the negative words and shift (pivot) to affirmations: "I give a voice to this emotion," "I honor my feelings," "I profoundly love and accept all of me;" "I choose to be calm and peaceful."

These can be frightening emotions for the client because admitting them may create more pain and problems. For this reason, many people would rather keep them locked into their "I don't want to go there" vault. That's why when they first begin Tapping, they may claim a safer and banal "I am upset."

As they continue Tapping, a person feels calmer, and it becomes safe to acknowledge their hidden emotions; they become more open to feeling what they have been denying. Soon, the beach balls of emotion start popping out of the water with the velocity of a cork coming off a champagne bottle. Eventually, more intense and visceral words start bursting out of their mouths, such as, "I am angry," "I resent," "I am jealous," and "I feel guilty." Occasionally, some f-bombs and tears spew out.

Continuing with the example of the adult child who is drinking, the emotion she stated was, "I am *upset* that my son is drinking again." (The word "upset" feels safer for this mother to say. It is a softer, more innocuous word and emotion.)

STM goes from Point A (unwanted emotion) to Point B (wanted emotion). Her A feeling would be that she is upset. Her B is what she wants to experience instead. Her B is that she wants to work through being upset so she can be at peace and enjoy her son, even though he is drinking again.

4. Create a Target Statement using the dilemma/stressor, emotion and adding where you feel the emotion in your body.

"When I think of _____ (above problem), I feel _____ (emotion) in my _____ (body part: chest, heart, stomach, etc.)."

The Target Statement is created by combining Steps 1 (problem/stressor), Step 3 (emotion) and identifying where in the body the person feels their emotions.

We identify where the emotion is located in her body. I would say, "When you think of your son's drinking, where do you feel this unease in your body? For example, do you feel it in your stomach, chest, neck, or another place?" If she doesn't know, you can continue the process without this information. However, if you can identify where the person feels the feeling in the body, you mention it in the Tapping. While moving through tapping points, say things like:

- "I feel all of these emotions in my stomach."
- "I can feel this anxiety (emotion) in my chest."

What the person presents with may differ from the core issue or actual emotion surrounding the dilemma. Even so, I started Tapping with what she believed was the issue.

Step 4: Target Statement: "When I think about my son's drinking again, I feel anxious in my stomach."

5. SUD—Rate the intensity of the emotion you feel in your body from one to ten, with ten having the most charge.

SUD score (intensity number) _____. Use this as a baseline score, and then, after several rounds of Tapping, compare the current SUD number to the initial SUD score.

The Subjective Unit of Distress (SUD) scale is a self-administered mechanism to rate the intensity of distress related to a specific emotion regarding the Tapping Target. Doctors often use this scale when they say, "On a scale of one to ten, how high is your pain?"

When you tap by yourself, it is unnecessary to determine a SUD score because you are in your own body and know if you feel better. However, as a practitioner, it is helpful to establish a client's baseline starting number to evaluate the progress and success of your current Tapping target. Tracking the SUD score answers the question, "Did we pick the correct emotion and aspect?"

The SUD scale ranges from one to ten. Establishing this baseline starting number helps you evaluate the progress and accuracy of the Tapping Target (dilemma) and emotion. The subsequent movement of the number in either direction indicates the accuracy and success of the current Tapping Target and subsequent Tapping. In other words, a change in the SUD number lets you know whether what you are Tapping on is the actual core issue and emotion or you are just beginning the discovery process.

I describe the SUD scale this way to my clients:

- Six is discomfort to the level that you desire a change.
- Seven is "It is irritating."
- Eight is, "It really bothers me."
- Nine is "I can't stop thinking about it, and it really bothers me."
- Ten is "It's huge."

You can create your own interpretation of the SUD scale or find one online. The key is consistency in how you rate and interpret that rating.

Going back to our example, I would ask the mother, "When you think of your son drinking again, how high is the anxiety charge in your body? A ten represents an intense sensation, while a one means you do not feel a charge at all."

Another way to say it is, "When you think of the problem or situation, how high is the charge in your body? An eight is, 'It really bothers me, and it's pretty intense,' while a ten is, 'It's off the charts.'"

Again, the precise accuracy of the rating isn't essential. The purpose of the SUD score is to track the progress of what I call "the charge," or bodily sensation, around the specific dilemma and emotion. Are we on target or not? Did something else come up? A different target (dilemma) or another emotion?

For example, if someone says, "My anxiety is a ten," we do a bit of Tapping on this emotion. If the number lowers, then we are on track for this dilemma and the anxiety surrounding it. We have identified and tapped on the accurate emotion for this problem.

Following the movement of the SUD score determines if we picked the correct Tapping Target and emotion.

In this situation, it confirms that the issue is the son's drinking and the coinciding emotion is anxiety. In another scenario, it could be the same dilemma, the son's drinking, but a different emotion, like anger or resentment. Either way, this is valuable information that you can use throughout the rest of the Tapping session.

If it doesn't move, there might be several explanations. These are addressed in Chapter Fifteen.

What If There Are Two Aspects and Dilemmas—Which Should I Choose?

I also use the SUD score to determine which topic and/or emotion has the most charge and will be my first Tapping topic.

For example, imagine the mother whose son is drinking again shares numerous emotions and aspects around her son's drinking. I would list them and ask her which has more charge right now.

"When you think of your situation with your son, you voiced several reasons you were upset and various emotions. Since I need a point to start the Tapping, it would be helpful if we identify one topic and emotion. These are some of the things I heard. Are you more upset because he is drinking again, embarrassed he looks terrible and is wandering the town streets, angry he isn't paying his wife for the children and forcing you to take on extra shifts at work so you can give them money, or resentful that you have already paid for treatment twice? Or is there something else?"

Or, if that feels overwhelming for the client, you could present it this way:

"Say this aloud and rate the feeling from one to ten, with ten having the most charge. 'When I think of my son's drinking problem, I am embarrassed he looks terrible and wanders the town streets.'" (She says six.)

Do the same with the following, "When I think of my son's

drinking problem, I am angry because he isn't paying his wife for the children, and I must give them money." (She states ten.)

I then start with the statement that has the highest SUD score. If a client says they are equal, I rotate each statement one by one through several Tapping Rounds. A Tapping Round is a one-time pass moving through all eight STM Tapping points. Tap on each emotion and aspect a bit and see if you can sift through to find the actual issue and emotion. Sometimes, what they present has nothing to do with what is causing them stress. Remember, the brain cheats and keeps you away from pain. For success, you discover the pain and Tap through it.

Hurt things hide.

SUD Number Changes

Let's say the SUD score shifts from ten to five. My interpretation of a SUD at a five translates to "It's not horrible, and I can live with it and learn more about why I am troubled by it." It creates an opening and choices. You can think a bit more clearly from a five and see alternative perspectives with the problem at hand. However, when you are above a SUD of a five, you are reacting to the half-truths and antiquated stories we tell ourselves stemming from long-ago experiences. It's like a castle drawbridge is up, covering your eyes and limiting your vision.

For example, if you fear setting a boundary with someone, you act a certain way, following patterns of interactions established long ago to avoid pain. However, if you lower this fear, you empower yourself to see more available choices. They might not be exciting, joyous options, but at least the drawbridge is down, and you see the entire landscape, not just the sliver of mulch under your toes.

Some people would be satisfied if a SUD dropped from a nine to a six, but I would want to discover why I can't set a boundary. Plus, knowing helps you make sense of your suffering and toxic behaviors. It is easier to change your behavior once you understand it.

This boundary-setting problem is likely rooted in an adverse childhood experience or possibly an identity issue stemming from a childhood belief. There are several reasons you might not be moving if you can't move below a six by Tapping. Please see Chapter Fifteen.

It's important to note that usually takes more than one round for a person to get into their body. Watch their face, look for a change, and then check again on their SUD score.

SUD Goes Up

A person may become more anxious during Tapping because they are now experiencing difficult emotions they have been suppressing, which can raise their SUD. This awareness is what causes their anxiety to rise. Remember, awareness is information.

It's a good sign in Tapping if the anxiety goes up because it means you have identified the core emotion and aspect.

6. Feel It—Start your Tapping at any EFT meridian point.
While Tapping, move through the tapping points while reading the above details (the content as you see it) and the emotions you currently feel. Tap, Talk, and Tell the truth.

Ask the client to go into their body, meaning they should focus more on the sensations in their body while Tapping instead of focusing on what they are saying.

7. Dump It—End your Tapping session on positive emotions by dumping the negative words and shift (pivot) to affirmations. Common ones used in Tapping are, "I give a voice to this emotion," "I honor my feelings," "I profoundly love and accept all of me," and "I choose to be calm and peaceful."

The only rule is that you never end a Tapping session when the inner critic is raging. If you find yourself still judging and berating yourself, you need to do several more rounds of tapping to deliberately shift to positive energy. (See "I Am Done Purging My Emotions, so What's Next?" in Chapter Twelve.)

People often ask me, "How do I know when a person should be, or is, done Tapping?" My answer is "How much time do you have?" Have you lowered the SUD score, or is there a new issue rising that you need to Tap on?

FT is a quick fix to lower anxiety for immediate clarity. STM, on the other hand, digs deeper into the root cause of one's feelings and beliefs. This insight may elicit strong emotions and uncover an exceptionally painful small "t" or traumatic memory requiring more Tapping Rounds and subsequent time to process and recover from their impact.

If you don't have time to process and recover from what you uncovered, I suggest you wait until you do have time. You may want to take a break from Tapping because STM Tapping can be emotionally exhausting. If this is the case, then I suggest that you Tap and acknowledge this need for a break, and then use forms of Happy Tapping to help you move on for now. You may want to contact a mental health professional to work with you on what you have discovered.

If your SUD doesn't go down, there could be several reasons for this. Look at Chapter Fifteen for more information on what to do if Tapping isn't working.

The Traditional EFT Protocol

The mental health professionals I have trained in Tapping find STM to be easier to learn, implement, and replicate than traditional EFT. That's why I have focused on it and FT in this book.

Performing traditional EFT requires two more steps than STM: the Set-Up Statement, which has two parts, and includes Tapping on something called the "Karate Chop point," also called the "Side of the Hand."

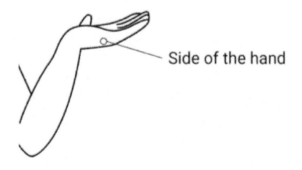

Side of the hand

You repeat your self-created and individualized Set-Up Statement three times while tapping on the Side of the Hand *before* you begin the Tapping Rounds. A Set-Up Statement is like the STM Target Statement with the addition of a positive affirmation. The affirmations can be anything, which is another reason people get confused with the traditional EFT protocol. Common ones are, "I give a voice to this emotion," "I honor my feelings," "I profoundly love and accept all of me," or "I choose to be calm and peaceful."

The Set-Up Statement is always stated as follows:

"Even though _____(dilemma/stressor statement), I _____(affirmation)."

You say the Set-Up Statement three times while tapping on your Side of the Hand.

Some examples:

"Even though I am upset my son is drinking again (dilemma/ stressor), I honor my feelings (affirmation)."

"Even though I am embarrassed he looks terrible and wanders the town streets, I profoundly love and accept all of me."

"Even though I am angry he isn't paying his wife for the children and I had to start giving them money, I choose to be calm and peaceful."

Repeat your set-up statement three times while tapping on your Side of the Hand.

You may think this one step that I don't include in STM doesn't seem so complicated. Please know that what I described above are examples of uncommonly sparse Set-Up Statements. In the traditional EFT protocol, this first step is highly stylized by each practitioner to the point it often includes extensive details and may go on for minutes. This creates an elaborate sequence of verbiage, which the client must repeat three times.

Try to have your clients duplicate this two-fold step, and see if they aren't more confused about EFT. I challenge you to watch different traditional EFT professionals performing the statement on YouTube. It's darn confusing. For various reasons, including the ones noted above, I only use the Set-Up Statement once in an entire Tapping session, if I use it at all.

Why I Prefer STM over Traditional EFT

When I work with clients on their issues, I first Tap through their concerns and negative thoughts and feelings before introducing any affirmations. Introducing affirmations like those included in the Set-Up Statement before the clients are open to hearing and receiving them can sometimes cause more harm than good. They are empty words offering no positive impact. Unbelievable affirmations can cause clients to resist and consciously, or unconsciously, make a case against them.

I also mostly use STM in my sessions because the Set-Up Statement ruins the flow of the session. If a person is sharing deeply and experiencing difficult emotions, it is unproductive to stop this natural release by inserting a structured phrase.

I am not alone in my use of not using the Set-Up Statement when Tapping. When I have employed master traditional EFT practitioners to work through some of my personal challenges, I've found they only use the Set-Up Statement one to two times in a session—if they use it at all.

If you aren't doing traditional EFT research and are only using Tapping with your clients, you may want to consider using FT and STM, not the full EFT protocol. Since they are less confusing there is a better chance that you and your clients will incorporate them more quickly into your lives.

However, if you do want to research and learn traditional EFT, knowing FT and STM will make the process of mastery so much easier.

Emotional Freedom Techniques (EFT)
Label It – Feel It – Dump It (LFD) System

1. Label It -- Describe the dilemma. What's bothering you? Finish this sentence: I am struggling with_____.

2. Label It -- The content. Write down details and thoughts about the dilemma/stressor. The more specific, the better. Or finish the sentence: I'm struggling with _____(above dilemma) because_____(the details/content as you see them).

3. Label It -- The emotion you feel when you think of the above struggle. You can pick a general emotion; however, for EFT to be most effective, you must uncover a core emotion. If you can't identify a core emotion, it should arise after some Tapping. "When I think of (dilemma), I feel (name emotion). And I feel this (emotion) in my __(name a body part: chest, heart stomach)."

- Examples of general emotions: upset, frustrated, overwhelmed, anxious, stressed, controlled, sad, unheard.
- Examples of core emotions: anger, fear, resentment, unloved, hurt, abandoned, shame.

4. SUD Score (number) -- Rate the intensity of the emotion you feel from one to ten, with ten having the most charge. Use this as a baseline SUD score, and then, after several Tapping Rounds, compare the current SUD (number) to the initial SUD. A Tapping round is one pass through the Tapping points. Example of a SUD score (intensity number): "The anxiety I feel in my stomach regarding the new job is an eight."

5. Feel It -- Create a Set-Up Statement. Repeat it three times while tapping on your Side of the Hand point before beginning the Tapping Rounds. This statement is your dilemma, emotion with a positive affirmation: Even though_____(stressor and emotion) I_____(affirmation)."

- Set-Up Statement example: "Even though I am hurt because _____, I honor my feelings anyway."
- Affirmation examples: I profoundly love and accept all of me, I choose to be calm and peaceful.

Begin the Tapping Round at any EFT point. While tapping, move through the points while reading the above details, including the emotion and where you feel the sensations in your body: "I feel all this hurt in my chest." Feel what you are saying. Tap, Talk, Tell the Truth. After several Tapping Rounds, compare the current SUD surrounding the issue to your baseline SUD score. The goal is to resolve or become less charged and more neutral to the dilemma. If new aspects and emotions arise, use the LFD system to address these.

6. Dump It -- End your Tapping session on positive emotions by dumping the negative words and shift (pivot) to affirmations: "I give a voice to this emotion," "I honor my feelings," "I profoundly love and accept all of me;" "I choose to be calm and peaceful."

For Tapping Videos, Search YouTube: Tijana Coso
*Duplication is permitted with attribution given to Tijana Coso
©Feb 2023 Tijana Coso, Tap@thetappingproject.com www.thetappingproject.com

☞ Key Concepts

- LFD is the framework of STM.

- Use FT during the discovery process.

- For STM to be most effective, seek to uncover core emotions, like anger, sadness, fear, rejection, loss, and abandonment.

- When Tapping, try to use specific details about the presenting problem.

- Use the SUD as a baseline to evaluate the accuracy of the Tapping target and track the progress of its continued relevance.

- Tapping may increase anxiety. All emotions are relevant messages.

CHAPTER 8

Using the Simple Tapping Method to Uncover a Small "t"

Where trauma impairs logical thinking, Tapping creates the ability to distinguish between the past and the present moment.

Robyn was an executive in her early sixties in a predominantly male field who contacted me seeking stress relief. Her anxiety had recently been so high that she visited the doctor several times. Before beginning medication to lower her anxiety, she wanted to try Tapping to see if it could help. Robyn didn't realize Tapping is more than a stress-relief tool. It's a BOGO (buy one, get one)!

In addition to lowering her stress response, Tapping would also provide cognitive insights into why she was suddenly having panic attacks.

As with any client, I started by gathering information. (The STM document outlined in Chapter Seven describes a detailed, step-by-step information-gathering process.)

The discovery process aims to gather the words, thoughts, and phrases to create a Target Statement and verbiage for a Tapping Script. A Target Statement is a statement of the target or problem the person is expressing, including the emotions they feel around it. Is the person experiencing anxiety, anger, or fear? The Tapping Script suggests words to say while Tapping with a person. It's not a script per se but a collection of keywords culled from the discovery and presented back to the client while leading them through Tapping. This script gives you, the practitioner, input on what to say, and then the client repeats your statements while tapping. In essence, the person is Tapping, Talking, and Telling the truth (3Ts); the truth is simply the information you gathered from the discovery. Or, more precisely, the "truth" they are telling themselves.

When Tapping on your own issues, use the same STM document. Instead of repeating information to a client, use the document as a guide to create a Tapping Script for yourself (more on this in Chapter Twelve).

Important to note: I showed Robyn FT before she started sharing her details about the dilemma. I do this because I want the client to have diminished anxiety and clearer thinking throughout our entire session, not just while we tapping on the problem. The second they begin speaking about the presenting issue, I ask them to start Tapping.

Exercise: Label It, Feel It, Dump It

Label It: Describe the dilemma (stressor) and its details. What's bothering you? Finish the sentence:

I am struggling with _____.

Robyn's answer: I am struggling with the anxiety I have been experiencing recently.

DISCOVERY PROCESS DIALOGUE

I liken the process and outcome of Tapping to the peeling of an onion. There are different layers in an onion, and when you peel back one layer, there is another and another until you get to the onion's core. Similarly, the STM process uncovers different triggers causing the anxiety until you discover the primary reason for the triggering.

I peel the onion back with a game of *I-Spy* while Tapping. If you are unfamiliar with this game, one person selects a random item in the room (like a red magnet on a refrigerator, for example), and the other person has to guess what it is by walking around the room. Directional clues come from the person who picked the item through temperature words, such as, "You are getting colder/warmer" or "You are getting hotter." When the person guessing is in the hot zone, they look around and begin to guess items nearby that could be the chosen item.

First Person: "Is it this red apple?"

Second Person: "No."

First Person: "Is it the red book?"

Second Person: "No."

First Person: "Is it the red magnet?"

Second Person: "Yes, you win! You discovered what it was."

Like in *I-Spy*, the words, thoughts, and phrases we gather during the discovery process become the clues to uncover the actual core emotions causing distress. In our game of *I-Spy*, we ask the questions, and the client goes into their body to give us the answers they feel are most accurate to their feelings.

Me: "Does it feel like sadness."

Client: "No."

Me: "Does it feel like anger?"

Client: "No."

Me: "Does it feel more like resentment?"

Client: "Yes, you win! You discovered what it was."

It's the same concept when you explore your own personal issues. Ask yourself the questions while Functional Tapping. Your words will bring your emotions to life.

Here's an inside secret about playing *I-Spy* with your brain: it cheats. Your survival brain will attempt to distract and throw you off course with lukewarm clues to keep you from getting close to uncovering your true feelings, especially if they aren't culturally appropriate or are something you wouldn't want to acknowledge or feel again. Remember, your survival brain protects you from pain. It is a justification and meaning-making machine that will construct unusual, creative, and seemingly ridiculous excuses to protect you from painful thoughts and actual reality. So, watch for the cheater brain to distract, conceal, or suppress genuine emotions. It doesn't play fair. To win in Tapping, you seek to discover the most visceral and often the most painful emotions regarding the presenting dilemma. Leading trauma experts, like Bessel van der Kolk and Peter Levine, contend that emotions that come to the surface can be healed.

What you feel, you can heal.

Your goal as a Tapping practitioner is to get more of a reaction from the person—not less of one. In other words, you want to increase the intensity of the emotions, not decrease them. As in the game *I-Spy*, you watch the client's reactions as you deliver the clues: words, thoughts, and phrases. In the Tapping session, you will sift and sort all the clues to discover insights that may lead you to the core issue, which offers the most opportunity for recovery with permanence.

If you don't move toward hotter emotions, a game of *I-Spy* may become months of Tapping on lukewarm clues tossed out by the survival brain for protection and deflection from the truth. The game would never reveal the actual aspect and core emotion surrounding the dilemma that continues to create unwanted reactions, behaviors, and feedback loops. Consequently, nothing permanently changes.

When you play the *I-Spy* Tapping game by yourself, you ask yourself and answer the questions by going into your body to feel the answers, not think about them. You seek the same goal as when working with clients—a visceral reaction.

For example, let's say I am sensitive when people question my decisions and beliefs, and I want to understand why I am this way to manage my reactions better.

I begin tapping.

Problem: When people challenge me on any topic, I become defensive.

Ask yourself:

Question: "Is it due to the humiliation I felt when my co-worker corrected me in front of my peers?"

Answer: "No."

Question: "Is it because it feels like the constant corrections I experienced as a child?"

Answer: "No."

Question: "Is it because of what happened in college and how it hurt?"

Answer: "No."

Question: "Is it because of what happened when I went to band camp and the fear of messing up my solo?"

Answer: "No. But you're getting warmer!"

When Tapping and peeling back layers, you often discover that various emotions are tied to the triggering event. With STM, once you uncover one aspect and specific emotion about a dilemma or circumstance, another may arise. In fact, a person's anxiety may rise with these discoveries instead of lowering. When this happens, it's a good indication that you are getting closer to the true issue. If you can keep peeling, get to the underlying issue, and work through it with Tapping, the problem becomes a non-issue. And sometimes, this can occur quickly from the new information gained from Tapping. What is fascinating and worth celebrating is when a person has presented an all-consuming worry, and in one Tapping session, the anxiety surrounding this issue is completely wiped out. They are so "over" whatever was causing intense anxiety that it doesn't appear as even a blip on their nervous system radar now. This is what eventually occurred with Robyn.

In the first session, I had her label the dilemma. Her answer was: I am struggling with the anxiety I have been experiencing recently.

The next step was for her to label (describe) the content through our game of I-Spy. I collected details and thoughts surrounding the dilemma, and wrote them down on the STM document. (You can also fill out this statement: I feel ____(emotion) about ____(problem) because ____(truth).)

ROBYN'S DIALOGUE WHILE FUNCTIONAL TAPPING

Robyn tapped as she explained, "I'm so stressed that I am losing control of my emotions. My husband thinks it's because I'm stressed about my daughter's upcoming wedding. Plus, I'm our condo association's president, and there's a major issue with a new condo owner. I went to the doctor, and she found nothing medically wrong with me. She thinks I'm going through situational stress, so she prescribed antianxiety medication. The peculiar thing is that I only have anxiety attacks at work. Which **doesn't make sense** because I've been at the same company for over nineteen years and this position for the last six, so it can't have anything to do with work. I have no idea what's going on."

Since she's been in the same job for years, I asked if something had changed in the last three to six months to trigger this increase in anxiety.

Still tapping, she explained that the only thing that had changed was a new person named Darrel had joined the executive team about three months ago. "He doesn't mistreat me in any way."

Tap, tap, tap.

(I noticed a little shift in her voice and more facial expressions of contemplation—clarity was rising.)

"However, for some reason, you're right. I feel a little more anxious whenever he's in a meeting with me. But that's probably just due to my increased anxiety [this is the brain justifying the anxiety]. I'm just not myself."

Things were changing as she spoke—I spied a red magnet (trigger). So, I explored the anxiety around the new employee. It's important to note that I never said anything about the problem stemming from the new executive. That was her revelation. As she tapped, she became more grounded and felt safer to experience her feelings, allowing awareness to arise.

She also expressed that Darrel has a big personality (faster tapping). And since he joined the company, she may feel a little less heard by the all-male executive team.

"Being the sole woman executive, I've always felt **less heard**. It's never bothered me because I exert myself when I believe my information is vital. Otherwise, I keep my mouth shut and leave my ego out of the meeting. But now that I think about it, since Darrel joined the team, when I speak up it feels different." Faster tapping. "I know it doesn't make sense, but sometimes **I feel different, like an insecure kid,** which is a new emotion. I am not insecure at all. This whole thing is a little odd. Because you're right, I change when he's around."

I wish I were wise enough to have suggested to Robyn that she changed when Darrel was around, but I never said that either. It came up while she was Tapping and talking—telling the story. It rose because the Tapping made her feel safe enough to have clarity.

As we explored more about her interactions with Darrel and how she felt, I could sense her emotions were escalating, and so was the speed of her tapping. She described how she physically felt a rush of anxiety in the pit of her stomach when Darrel entered the meeting room.

Below is more of the dialog from the discovery process, where Robyn describes what happens when she encounters Darrel. As you read this, I want you to imagine a successful female executive who is slightly exasperated and embarrassed while sharing this story. However competent normally, while talking to me, Robyn didn't look like an accomplished woman. As she tap, tap, tapped, she seemed more like a fearful, naïve, and bewildered person.

"Wow, this is interesting. I don't understand it, but I realize now that my panic starts when I'm around Darrel or need to interact with him. We have weekly management meetings, and he is part of the team now, so I have more exposure to him."

I asked her to continue tapping and telling me (Talk) about her anxiety in the meetings. I said, "Try to imagine yourself in this meeting. Describe the scenario and what you feel."

"We gather in one of our executive meeting rooms. We are seated around a large conference table. Oh my gosh, this is ridiculous. I don't know what just happened, but I felt my anxiety jump and my chest tighten while describing this!"

Robyn looked at me, slightly panicked and confused. I asked her to take a moment to calm down if she needed it and keep tapping without talking. Once she was settled, I explained again that if she felt too anxious, she could stop talking, continue tapping, and, if more helpful, open her eyes. She nodded, and we continued.

"Once the last person enters the meeting room, the administrative secretary closes the door." Robyn took a big breath, like she was struggling to breathe, and began to shake her head before continuing. **Once I hear the click of the door closing, my heart starts racing, and I feel like I can't breathe.** I know it sounds wild, but I can feel myself starting to panic right now."

Me: "Keep tapping. How do you feel?"

Robyn: "I don't know." Pause and another deep breath. "I just **feel like I am trapped. I want to break out of the meeting room and run away.**" She opens her eyes. "How weird is that? There is something seriously wrong with me. **I know it sounds wild. I am so embarrassed that, at my age, I am reacting like this. It just doesn't make any sense. Maybe it is time for me to think about retiring.**"

Trauma hint: how many successful sixty-two-year-olds say they want to run out of a meeting because they feel trapped in an office? By Tapping and Talking, connections from the past link and emerge.

DISCOVERY INFORMATION COLLECTED, NOW WHAT?

The words I highlighted in bold were the emotionally charged words and phrases I gathered and noted on the STM document. This information is what I repeated back to her in the Tapping session as part of the Tapping Script.

Below are some of the key phrases from Robyn's dialogue:

- I don't feel heard.
- I feel like an insecure child.
- What's wrong with me?
- I feel trapped.

ESTABLISH A SUBJECTIVE UNIT OF DISTRESS (SUD) SCORE

Robyn initially presented with general anxiety not linked to anything specific. Using FT during the discovery process connected her anxiety to work and, more specifically, the new employee Darrel. So even though I heard other possible causes (reasons) for her unease, I started with the anxiety surrounding the new employee, Darrel.

The next step was to discover Robyn's SUD surrounding her anxiety with Darrel. I encouraged her to close her eyes, tap, and go into her body to feel her answer, not just think about it. I also asked if she felt her anxiety anywhere specific in her body.

Me: "Robyn, I'm going to ask you to repeat a sentence after me while tapping and end it with a number between one and ten, with ten being the highest. When considering your answer, pay attention to where in your body you feel your anxiety. 'When I think about the anxiety I feel in a meeting with Darrel, my anxiety feels like a ___.'"

Robyn: "Well, during the last two meetings he attended, I left in the middle of the meeting and went directly to the emergency room because I feared I was having a heart attack. I had no idea my anxiety was due to Darrel being in the room. I thought it was just stress-related, not Darrel-related."

Me: "Okay. Well then, let's give you a number of ten."

Robyn: "A twenty! I'm feeling panic rising in my chest right now." Tap, tap, tap.

STM TAPPING SESSION

Once the aspect (anxiety with Darrel) and the SUD number were established, I led Robyn through a Tapping session, letting her choose if she wanted to keep her eyes open or closed. I said the phrases written on the STM document, and she repeated them while we repeatedly tapped, moving through each of the eight meridian points.

As I led her and we tapped, her breathing got faster. Her head was down and shaking left to right. Occasionally, when I repeated specific phrases, she looked up at me with slight panic as she repeated the anxiety-inducing words. I've seen that look many times. It's the expression of a person silently communicating, "Please. Don't make me go there."

However, in Tapping, we lean into and through pain. If the process had become too painful, we could have stopped talking, and she would have continued tapping until her emotions were regulated and she felt comfortable enough to move on. Interestingly, once people know they can control or modulate the intensity of their rising emotions, they tend not to stop the process. They may pause for a second to cry, but they don't retreat because they feel in control of the experience.

We continued repeatedly tapping on the meridian points while re-stating her words, and she underwent and tolerated heightened anxiety. However, there was no moment of clarity where she said, "Oh, I see why I am so anxious." Neither was there a reduction of anxiety. In the game of I-Spy, I equate this to being warm on the aspect but not hot. I knew something was going on because of her bodily responses, but we hadn't identified what I like to call the "golden nugget," which is the core reason for the anxiety. I needed to explore other emotions or aspects of the problem. I needed to poke around a bit to get a "hot" reaction.

I probed by inserting something I call a "Leading Phrase," a thought or idea I use to lead the client to the point of connection to something.

We went through the following phrases (which were her original words), which I said first and then she repeated:

- "I don't feel heard."

- "I feel like a teenager."

- "What's wrong with me?"

- "The second the door clicks, I feel panic in my stomach, and my heart starts racing. I can't breathe." (As Robyn repeated this, she put her other hand on her chest while tapping.)

- "I have a fear that I am trapped."

- "I want to run away."

- "I need to get out of here."

- "I feel trapped."

- "I want to run away, but I can't."

- "I feel trapped, and I can't get out."

Then I added the Leading Phrase: "I feel trapped, **just like when...**"
I paused, waiting for her to finish repeating the Leading Phrase I inserted. Her head popped up. She stopped shaking her head, froze, and locked her eyes on mine. Bingo! A memory was surfacing, so I repeated the leading phrase.

Me: "I feel trapped, **just like when...**"
Robyn: "Oh my God."
A wide-eyed, shocking recognition crossed her face, and tears came. The *I-Spy* game was over. Robyn won.

We live the body's memory.

She started crying and told me about a childhood incident that, for some reason, reminded her of the current situation in the meeting room with Darrel.

Robyn: "It's outrageous, but a childhood memory came up, and with it, the same sick anxiety feeling I get when I'm in the meeting room with Darrel."

An experience that had unknowingly left a lasting physiological and psychological impact on her.

Robyn's Small "t"

I spy something in my past
that is causing me to panic.

I had Robyn tap as she explained her childhood memory so she wasn't flooded with unbearable emotions.

Robyn's mother died when she was four, and her father raised her and her brother. When she was fourteen years old, she babysat for a neighbor. The children's father always picked her up when she sat for them. Since this was back in the sixties, it was proper for the father to open Robyn's car door for her and close it. Robyn explained that he would walk to the driver's side and get in. When his door clicked shut, he would lean over, slide his hand to her thigh, and rub it up and down while asking her how she was doing.

"His behavior was not a casual pat on the leg."

This happened several times. Eventually, she got the courage to tell her father. Back then, children didn't talk about such things, and definitely not with a father. Her dad brushed it off and told her she was overreacting and that the father was just being friendly. However, she knew otherwise. So, she felt **unheard**.

The following week, the children's father stretched his arm over and did it again on the way back to her house after babysitting. She hurriedly tried to exit the car, but he held her leg down, restricting her from leaving. He didn't go farther with his hand. He rested it there while he made small talk with her.

At this point in the story, Robyn looked at me with tears and, while tapping, said, "I was **trapped,** and all I wanted to do was break out of the car **and run away.**"

(Those are the exact words she used when she first spoke to

me and described her current situation in the executive meeting.)

> *"Trauma cannot exist without terror and helplessness." —Bessel van der Kolk*

This was when an emotional shift occurred for Robyn. The connections were made, and a look of recognition flashed across her face.

"Oh, my God! My panic attacks don't have anything to do with Darrel. Something about him reminds me of the predator father. So that's why I get anxious around him. Oh my God, isn't that bizarre?"

Trauma can emerge as a mixture of physical, mental, and emotional elements. What perplexes survivors is that the symptoms often don't appear until years later.

"In a way, I can see where he reminds me of the dad who groped me. He's stocky, dark-haired, and doesn't understand normal social distance when communicating, just like the dad I babysat for. So I somewhat understand the connection to my past. What baffles me is why the experience with the predator dad had such an impact on me because nothing happened but a little groping. I mean, nothing horrible happened. I wasn't raped or anything."

(I imagine some of you are familiar with this trauma discounting.)

Robyn had never connected her anxiety to her past childhood trauma. And why would she? In her mind, nothing happened. Right?

> *Our past is calling us back to find a resolution.*

Tapping Aids in Awareness

Our understanding of the world is unconsciously encoded in our emotional brain (nervous system). Even though Robyn's Thinking Brain never acknowledged what happened to her (a small "t"), her body and nervous system remembered. Her panic attacks revealed an unhealed trauma that was alive and present in her body.

Trauma research suggests that the event altered vital structures in her brain, creating an inability to distinguish between the past and the present experience.

This sort of small "t" discounting is what makes small "t"s so insidious. Even though they remain outside our awareness, they can create lasting psychological impacts because the body remembers their significance. This limbic reaction drives continual irrational and unwanted behavior that inevitably shapes one's life because adverse events that aren't processed become deep learning.

What if Robyn had never uncovered this small "t" and continued to have anxiety attacks at work? Her health and mental fortitude had already deteriorated. She possibly would have gone on medication, or, more drastically, her panic attacks may have forced her to rethink her career and convinced her to retire. Ultimately, her anxiety stemming from this childhood event blocked her from growth and interfered with her ability to live her best life. She had become a prisoner of her past.

With these more minor, less obvious small "t"s, people often blame themselves for their unwanted or self-destructive behaviors. When people can't connect the dots and see the source of their anxiety, depression, anger, mood swings, or eating disorders, they assume they are weak, crazy, broken, or something is simply wrong with them.

We are each a product of our environment and upbringing; these unwanted character traits aren't defects. They are a means we've developed to live within our circumstances. This insight allows for more self-acceptance and compassion.

Where trauma impairs logical thinking,
Tapping creates the ability to distinguish
between the past and the present moment.

Peeling the Onion

The curious thing with Tapping is that once the intensity surrounding a particular issue is lowered, another layer of the onion is peeled back, which may reveal a different emotion occurring from the same situation.

Initially, Robyn contacted me because of general anxiety. Then, after a bit of Functional Tapping during the discovery process, she realized her anxiety specifically surrounded her interactions with Darrel. Then the small "t" insight occurred. Once we Tapped on the issue of her past childhood trauma, new troubling emotions arose: shame and guilt. Incidentally, all this awareness was uncovered in the same session.

Victims of violence often think they are responsible for what happened to them. They wonder if they somehow encouraged the inappropriate behavior. However, that isn't why Robyn felt shame and guilt.

Robyn's shame and guilt had nothing to do with the childhood incident or the belief that she somehow encouraged the groping by the children's dad. Her feelings came from the current situation with Darrel. Her shame and guilt originated from self-judgment of her inappropriate and unprofessional behavior toward him—a contradiction of her values.

"What is wrong with me that this childhood situation from nearly fifty years ago is impacting me now? This is ridiculous, and I'm so embarrassed. You must think I'm a basket case. Plus, nothing happened!"

Robyn was ashamed that she didn't have control over her emotions. She felt guilty because she knew she treated Darrel differently because of her bias. She admitted she didn't overtly treat him wrong, but her dislike for him probably was evident on her face and in her mannerisms. She never supported the suggestions or ideas he presented to the executive team. She had an unconscious bias against someone who never did anything to her.

"I feel terrible that this man didn't do anything bad to me, and I treated him like he had." I told Robyn to celebrate the knowing, and I don't say that lightly. Robyn is lucky she was able to identify this small "t." She also is fortunate to recognize the secondary aspects (shame and guilt) surrounding her small "t" and be able to use FT to release them. Shame and guilt bore inward. They will make you sick and create out-of-balance behaviors.

Possibly you can identify with this concept. Have you ever felt a little ashamed or guilty about something? Nothing significant, just something you wish you didn't say or do. Or maybe something you wish you HAD said or done.

Before learning Tapping, I would turn my critical voice inward if I did something that did not align with who I wanted to be. Then, to assuage my guilt, I would overcompensate. I would over-give, say, or do. Since I discovered Tapping, I have been able to quickly assess the situation and decide if I need to apologize or if I'm being overly self-critical and must let go and move on.

Guilt and shame are heavy burdens to carry. Use Tapping to lighten the load and love yourself more.

After a bit of tapping on Robyn's shame surrounding her bias against Darrel, we checked her SUD score. It had dropped to a five. Her Tapping homework was to continue FT to interrupt her self-critical thoughts and soften and break her reactive thinking patterns.

As we were closing her first session and circling back to her small childhood "t," Robyn also realized this wasn't the first time she had felt trapped without options. She recalled how she felt trapped with a college roommate to whom she couldn't say no. She also felt trapped on various corporate and nonprofit boards. Eventually, at the end of the session, Robyn shared feelings of being trapped in her marriage. Her husband is an alcoholic, and she often thought about divorcing him. In Tapping, we call repeat patterns of emotion a "theme."

Obviously, in each of the situations noted above, Robyn had choices; however, her trauma theme diminished her ability to see them. Consequently, her unconscious pattern of feeling trapped paralyzed her from making healthy life changes. Whether it was simply quitting a position on a nonprofit board or exploring options for her marriage, Robyn froze.

Knowing her trauma theme will prove helpful. Now, when Robyn gets in situations where she feels trapped and without options, she will hopefully recognize that this unease stems from her pattern of feeling trapped and step back to Tap and reflect. There are always choices available in every instance, ranging from ideal to stressful but not life-threatening.

At the end of our time, Robyn scheduled a second session because she didn't believe this calm would last. She also wanted to work on the situation with her husband. Two weeks later, at our next session, I inquired about her anxiety surrounding Darrel. Her response would seem astonishing to anyone except an experienced EFT practitioner.

Looking confused, she said, "My husband's name is Daniel, not Darrel."

I reminded her that she initially contacted me about the problem with Darrel, not her husband. I said, "Darrel, the executive who caused you to go to the ER twice."

Instant recall appeared on her face. "Oh my goodness, I know it sounds ridiculous, but I'm completely over that. It's a nonissue.

What I really want to work on are the challenges with my husband and what to do."

I'm sure some of you are rolling your eyes, not believing the outcome of this story. I understand, but I promise I am not exaggerating one bit. Once you start working with Tapping, you will occasionally experience what we call a "one and done."

The One and Done: Instant Shift Using Tapping to Uncover a Small "t"

In some instances, by continually interrupting repetitive negative thoughts with Tapping, connections in the brain are broken. Over time, the anxious thoughts you are trying not to think about will fade. Eventually, these troubling associations become only a tinge of a sensation.

On the other hand, sometimes people experience an instantaneous and complete emotional shift to peace. Here's the way I see it: if an adverse event or experience can instantly create a new connection in a person's brain, why can't the opposite be true? Why can't Tapping immediately break the very same synaptic connections?

A one-and-done often occurs when a small "t" surfaces. This new information creates a sudden shift as matters are seen in a new light and through a new adult lens.

☞ Key Concepts

- Use STM to uncover small "t"s.

- Tapping helps you pass the litmus test of pain avoidance.

- The STM document can be used for personal and professional purposes.

- By Tapping and Talking, connections from the past are linked and emerge.

- As a practitioner, it is helpful to establish a client's baseline SUD score (number) to evaluate the progress and success of your chosen Tapping aspect.

- Tracking the SUD score answers the question, "Did we pick the correct Tapping emotion or aspect?"

- When you Tap by yourself, it is not necessary to determine a SUD score because you are in your own body and know if you feel better or not.

- In STM, we are seeking to discover what triggers a person while also offering Tapping for calming.

- Where trauma impairs logical thinking, STM creates the ability to distinguish between the past and the present moment.

- When the small "t" is cleared, the visceral reaction no longer occurs.

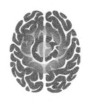

CHAPTER 9

The Components for Change Awareness, Acceptance, and Action (3As)

"I've chosen my epitaph. God, grant me the serenity to accept the things that I cannot change, and I want this change right now." —Anonymous

I borrowed the 3As, what I call the Components for Change, from Al-Anon Family Groups, an organization that helps people impacted by a friend or loved one's alcoholism. I use the components for change as an overarching framework throughout the Tapping process. Whenever you are Tapping and ask yourself "What should I do now," turn to the 3As for direction.

The First "A": Awareness

*The behavior you aren't aware of
is much harder to manage.*

The first "A" is awareness. Identifying and labeling unwanted, and sometimes painful, thoughts and emotions are the cornerstone and foundation of change. You can't change what you don't know. Once you know something, you can address it.

From Tapping, you may discover that your low self-esteem is because your parents never believed in you as much as they did your brother. This new knowledge alone may not give you the confidence to improve your life. It merely explains why you procrastinate on moving ahead with your goals, pursuing your passions, or value yourself enough to set healthy boundaries.

This awareness may also lead to other insights, such as why you get irritated instead of being happy for your brother when he announces his new work promotion to the family. It may also explain why you praise your daughter more than your son, push her to get better grades, and encourage her to seek a career in engineering like your brother instead of teaching which she has expressed an interest.

This knowledge may also explain why you have unconsciously created a distance between you and your only sibling. Sadly, like the situation with Robyn and her bias against her co-worker Darrel, your brother did nothing to deserve any of this.

Information (awareness) is only
the first step in the Tapping process.

The Second "A": Acceptance

"Neuroscience research shows that the only way we
can change the way we feel is by becoming aware of
our inner experience and learning to befriend what
is going on inside ourselves." —Bessel van der Kolk

The second "A" of the process is acceptance. If you've turned to Tapping, you desire to address a problem and seek change. A change from angst to peace, confusion to clarity, unwanted to wanted.

The very word "change" requires something different to happen. What is confounding is that the opposite is needed for emotional and behavioral changes. Change happens when you first accept your current reality, including unwanted thoughts, beliefs, and emotions. It's often referred to as the "paradox of change."

Van der Kolk suggests befriending what is happening inside us as a mechanism to heal trauma. When I think of befriending something, I envision embracing it. Here is the challenge: how do you befriend and embrace what you don't want to acknowledge, let alone accept?

Accepting anything undesirable, like the fact that you're jealous because your brother was blatantly loved more by your parents, is not something we humans like to do. Pain-aversion principles are deeply rooted in the evolution of human behavior. Our thinking goes like this, "An uncomfortable and painful thing threatens to rise into my conscious awareness. I need to take action to quickly suppress or distract myself before I feel any discomfort."

When I explain the second "A" (acceptance) in my training, I sometimes get a little pushback. "First, you want me to talk about my negative traits, which is difficult enough. Now you want me to accept them? How does this help? It makes me feel like I'm stuck and a victim." Humans have a primordial need to act and problem-solve. If there is a problem, we are predisposed to fix it. However, with Tapping, the opposite is desired. It is less effective if you attempt to coerce, manipulate, or, as I like to say, "effort" change before you accept or befriend your reality or current beliefs. Until we Tap to accept what we feel right now, change will not occur. You won't get over your hurt, anger, jealousy, biases, or self-judgment.

Tapping on acceptance is the key to change, even if the emotions or beliefs we are Tapping on don't make sense to us or are inaccurate, culturally unacceptable, or simply a story we are telling ourselves. What's required to initiate change is only to acknowledge and honor our feelings and thoughts, not argue for their logic or accuracy. When we Tap for acceptance, we are not joyfully proclaiming our newfound acceptance of the very thing we don't want to accept. We are merely admitting, and no longer denying, our truth about how we feel at this specific moment.

I think of the paradox of change like those straw finger traps I had as a child. You put your finger in each end, and the more you struggle to pull your fingers out, the tighter the straw weaving constricts until your fingers are stuck inside. You must do the opposite of what is logical to extract your fingers. They release only after you push both fingers inward, deeper into the trap.

When we stop fighting with our thoughts and feelings and thrust ourselves into our secret truths, change occurs effortlessly and organically. It's like dropping the rope in a tug-of-war game. Think of how much energy it takes to resist reality, not to mention all of the unhealthy avoidance behaviors we employ to maintain our ignorance.

Resistance to reality shows up in our behaviors.

The constant strain depletes our mental and emotional resources. Once we drop the rope and move to acceptance, we have more clarity to problem solve and can seek more advantageous outcomes.

Often when we Tap for acceptance of a situation, unforeseen opportunities become available because we are no longer closing ourselves off from them. When a person responds from a place of ease and openness, strange things happen that they would never have expected. Doors open, other people change, relationships improve, or they find their ideal job, pair of shoes, or even partner.

Sometimes the outcome of Tapping for acceptance isn't about change. It is about having the ability to relate to the issue differently. You become neutral to what "is" and respond from a place of calm embodiment.

I ask my workshop attendees to list things they don't want to accept. The items range from an illness, irresponsible behavior, past traumas, financial debt, and watching a loved one suffer to getting a speeding ticket, missing a flight, not setting a boundary, and gaining thirty pounds. Tapping on the acceptance of these is not going to change anything. The curious thing is that once we accept the current reality of this moment, we can relate to it differently.

Please understand that Tapping on acceptance does not mean we are settling or being victims. It also does not mean submission to a degrading situation or claiming powerlessness. Tapping for acceptance is coming to a space of acceptance of the current moment. It is acknowledging and honoring our feelings, not believing in their logic.

The Third "A": Action

The third "A" represents action, which is the actual change or shift of energy. Here's the twist. Action isn't a step, exercise, or skill. It is what naturally occurs if you implement the first two As.

By becoming aware and then truly and deeply accepting what you have worked hard not to accept, an emotional shift will organically occur. This shift, the "action step," occurs without the mental gymnastics of trying or "efforting" for change.

Using the 3As

The 3As are your guidepost when you're unsure of the next step in the Tapping process. The order of the 3As must be maintained. For example, if you or your client are aware of a core issue and emotion, or become aware of it from using STM, the next step is acceptance. By tapping on accepting, acknowledging, or honoring the truths currently believed, something within a person shifts (action of some type occurs). The change could be a degree of peace they may immediately experience from Tapping, or they may experience it more subtly over time.

In a single Tapping session with my clients, we may cycle through the 3As numerous times on various issues. Whenever a different buried truth is discovered while Tapping, we work it through the 3As again.

Let's say I am working with a client, Tapping on a specific quarrel she had with her parents that she can't seem to get over. Using the STM, she realizes the argument isn't about the current conflict but a pain stemming from her childhood. There were unhealthy dynamics in her household when she was growing up, and both parents mistreated her. They didn't talk to her when they were angry with her. They weren't interested in having a relationship with or even raising her.

Additionally, it wasn't her imagination that her brother was treated better. They jokingly told her they loved him more, and the truth was reflected in their treatment of her. Not being loved by one's parents is the type of awareness no one would want to admit or embrace, let alone accept.

By using STM, we accomplished the first "A." We are aware of the core issue arising from her argument with her parents. They didn't love her. Through additional Tapping Rounds, we process this significant pain and hurt. She can tap on specific events and images, or she can tap on the overall pain and sadness.

To Tap on acceptance, you witness, honor, and accept the emotions surrounding this pain and loss by Tapping, Talking, and Telling the truth (3Ts). This sort of Tapping is excruciatingly heartbreaking. It requires deep, profound vulnerability and honesty. Below is a general idea of what Tapping might look like when attempting to accept the truth that your parents did not, and possibly still don't, love you.

- "I wasn't loved."

- "I wasn't even liked."

- "I can't believe I am stating what I have always known and fought to deny."

- "My parents didn't love me at all."

- "I am so deeply hurt."

- "I am devastated by this."

- "I can't get over it."

- "I fear that I will never get over the fact that my parents don't love me and never will."

After crying and purging, I would shift to more neutral language. These are words of acceptance:

- "How I was treated as a child was horrible."

- "The pain is profound."

- "And this is something I cannot change."

- "I wish I could go back and change it, but I can't."

- "I don't know if I will ever get over it."

- "I am only stating it out loud."

- "And this is all I am capable of right now."

While Tapping, another feeling may arise, like anger, jealousy, or shame. These would need to be addressed with the STM process focusing on the new Tapping Target and SUD. The daughter would use STM to work through her anger. If the pain of the hurt continues after this Tapping, we will turn to the second "A" acceptance. We would tap on accepting her anger, just like we did on how not being loved made her feel.

The action of the 3As may not change anything other than lessening the intense emotions surrounding the issue. In the example above, my client can't change how her parents currently treat her or how they mistreated her as a child. However, by Tapping and accepting what is, change will occur. She will change the way she shows up and interacts with her parents. Their lack of love will not trigger her. Additionally, her relationship with her brother will improve because her jealousy of him will dissipate. By Tapping on this issue as many times as needed, the lens of being unlovable that has colored her life and experiences will change.

☞ Key Concepts

- The 3As are a guide to navigating Tapping.

- The order of the 3As must be maintained.

- The first "A" is awareness. Awareness of the dilemma is the first step to change.

- Sometimes, we are aware of what the issue is. When it's buried below our level of awareness, STM can be used to uncover it.

- The second "A" is acceptance.

- Tapping for acceptance is acknowledging and honoring our feelings, not believing in their logic.

- You can't change without accepting your current emotions, yet change is accepting your thoughts and the reality of the current situation. This is known as the "paradox of change." Tapping overcomes this paradox.

- The third "A" is action. Change naturally occurs with acceptance.

PART TWO

DIVING DEEPER INTO TAPPING

CHAPTER 10

The Magnificent Mind

*Tapping is a brain-savvy
approach to self-regulation.*

Is it possible to geek out over neuroplasticity? Even though it seems like a big, fancy word, neuroplasticity simply means the brain can change. Scientists no longer believe our brains are fixed machines, running the single operating system programmed into our psyches during childhood. Through learning, the brain is constantly changing those connections.

Those changes occur in what is called the "synaptic connections."

Synapses Linking, Thoughts Fading

When I think of synaptic connections, I imagine paths in the brain connecting one thought to another. Let's say you put a small herb garden and flower bed in your backyard to the left of the property. Every day, you walk to that plot and water. Over time, a path is worn into your grass to that little piece of mother nature. Several years later, a friend with a green thumb looks at your backyard and suggests, "You know, there is more direct light on the right side of your backyard. You may want to try growing your plants over there instead."

Equipped with this new information, you give it a try. You abandon the left garden plot and relocate your plants to a new area on the right side of your yard. You discover your friend was right, so you keep the garden on the right side of your property. Since you now turn right out of your back door, the left path (synaptic connection) is no longer being used and starting to fade. Instead, you are slowly developing a new connection through repeated walks to the right.

Scientists describe this as "firing and wiring" new brain circuits that reflect the new understanding. In response to the latest information and experiences, the brain must reorganize neural pathways to align with the new knowledge. New paths are built while old ones no longer in use die off. This is called "pruning."

When we change how we think and what we believe about a traumatic experience, reframing it in a different, healthier light, we loosen the connection to the negative, harmful thoughts. As with the garden example, the grass fills in the path, and the link is lessened to the point where you may barely notice the old path to the left.

Sometimes, instant changes occur instead of this slow overwriting, as we talked about with small "t"s. When this happens, people say, "A switch is flipped." Similar to when you feel a certain way about a character or plot device in a movie, and then suddenly, usually near the end of the film, a complete shift occurs, and the character you once despised suddenly becomes the true hero.

This immediate shift using Tapping occurs more often than you might think. The combined Tapping and Talking process can quickly and permanently break the connections to past painful memories, allowing newer, healthier ones to form.

Tapping shifts your energy instead of having to manipulate your thoughts.

Tapping: Creating a Pause

When the intense emotions surrounding an issue haven't completely subsided and continue to cause agitation, I recommend constantly interrupting the thought pattern with FT. You can use FT to press pause on long-established harmful patterns of thought and create a gap that gives you space to enable new rational thinking. Consider it as a way to rewire your nervous system.

Let's say that every time you think **Thought A**, your body reacts because it automatically connects it to **Thought B**. Your goal with FT is to interrupt the connection. Don't worry about what to say. Just tap to interrupt the connection. This type of Tapping is not expected to "cure" anything. The goal is to take away the power these thoughts have to grab and control your attention.

You may wonder how often you need to do this unwiring exercise. Well, I'll ask you this. Are you sick and tired of obsessing over these repetitive, anxiety-inducing thoughts? If the answer is yes, then I say, "Often."

I don't know if this ever happens to you, but sometimes I just can't let go of something. I seem to be tapping and talking about this annoyance like a pebble in a shoe so frequently that I get disgusted with myself. Exasperated with the redundancy of my personal Tapping narration, I eventually cry out and talk to myself, "Stop already! I know, Tijana, that you think XYZ (negative thought). I got it."

Tap, tap, tap. "What happened wasn't fair, and I am so sorry for you, but can we just let it go for a little bit? Maybe focus on something else for a couple of minutes?" Tap, tap, tap.

Then I continue Tapping, shift from my self-critical voice verbiage, and enlist help from my loving self.

"I am sorry, Tijana. I know it was painful." Tap, tap, tap. "Is it okay if we move on? I just want peace for you." Tap, tap, tap. After a bit of this loving dialogue, I smile as if my dearest love had said those words to me, like another happy ending to a Hallmark movie.

Let's look at some examples of harmful thought patterns, all of which are real examples from clients. Please notice how none of the B thoughts are helpful. They may honestly represent how a person feels, but they aren't helpful.

Thought A	Thought B
My son may have an addiction problem.	I have a fear he may die.
I feel like something is off with my health.	I have a fear I may have fibromyalgia/multiple sclerosis/cancer like my sister/mother/friend has.
I want to apply for a new job.	I have a fear I am not good enough. I need another degree or certification. I am not smart enough. I am not attractive enough. I am too old.
I have a fear of setting a boundary with my _____.	They may get angry with me and won't talk to me like my mother did. They will think I am selfish. They won't love me.
I fear divorcing my abuser.	Because I will never find another partner.

Instead, every time Thought A occurs, a person would begin tapping to interrupt the anxiety signal going to the brain and break the connection between the two thoughts.

Rewiring a Foster Child's Fear with Tapping

A six-year-old foster child, who we'll call ShaNay, living in rural Appalachia became anxious when she took long car rides. She had been in seven foster homes in six years, which is traumatic in and of itself. Her current foster parents adopted her a year prior. ShaNay would get anxious on long car rides because she feared she was traveling to a new foster home.

Thought A	Thought B
This is a long car ride.	I have a fear I might not come home to my adoptive parents.

Her parents assured her she was adopted, and they were her parents now and forever. But this fear of long car rides was wired into her nervous system, and words were no match for bodily terror. Bessel van der Kolk would say her body, not her mind, was keeping the score, and she was convinced the game would end with her being delivered to a different foster home.

Whenever Thought A came into her mind, Thought B automatically showed up as well.

Thought A: This is a long car ride.

Thought B: I am getting dropped off at a new foster home.

The Tapping homework plan for this family addressed the anticipatory stress with FT to loosen the trauma-trigger connections. As soon as the parents knew they were going for a long (over twenty minutes) car ride, they would start Functional Tapping to deal with the anticipation anxiety.

It looked like this:

The mother starts tapping on herself as soon as she begins talking to the child. Modeling the behavior prompts ShaNay to also start tapping.

Mother: ShaNay, we are going to grandma's house this Sunday. You know that is a long car ride.

ShaNay looks at her mother with wide eyes, and fear crosses her face.

Mother: Do you feel that anxiety in your belly again?

A spurt of anxious, fast nods from ShaNay.

Mother: Well, let's keep Tapping and have a conversation with your belly.

This conversation labels feelings and emotions. A couple of phrases acknowledging the feelings and fears I suggested were:

- "Of course my belly might be feeling anxious. My belly doesn't have a brain, so it doesn't understand I will stay with mommy and daddy forever and ever."

- "They will never give me back."

- "This is only a car ride to grandma's."

- "I live here; I am part of this family."

The mother reminded ShaNay to tap every time she thought about the long trip to her grandmother's house. With Tapping, we don't suppress or distract ourselves from pain but move toward and through it. For this reason, I encouraged the mother not to avoid the topic of ShaNay's fear of being moved to a different foster home.

I also suggested that throughout the preceding week, the mother bring up the upcoming car ride to ShaNay when they had time to Tap and Talk. The goal was to expose this trigger in order to decrease the sensitivity surrounding it.

However, why only offer FT to address this child's upcoming fear? I recommended what I call "Trifecta Tapping": Functional Tapping before, during, and after the car ride. The mother begins tapping with ShaNay before they ever get into the car to address the anticipatory stress. Then, while riding in the car, ShaNay tackles the long trek's current panic with FT. Finally, they have a follow-up FT session to process any lingering thoughts or emotions from the entire experience of the visit to Grandma's house.

But why stop there? How about a Quadfecta—four wins? In addition, a therapist could use STM to have the child explore and process other car rides before she was adopted.

At one point, I worked with a younger foster child with similar anxiety in the stomach, and this little girl said she was angry that her belly was making her sick. She called her belly stupid for not understanding. Eventually, after Tapping with me for a while, she had a wonderfully loving conversation with her stomach instead of calling it names. This self-soothing is a lifelong gift she can bring into every negative encounter. This is why I say Tapping is a life-changing gift that keeps on giving.

In stressful, triggering moments, you always have relief at your fingertips. Break those old paths and build new ones to green gardens, and your mind will flourish with tending and care.

☞ Key Concepts

- Neuroplasticity means the brain can change with new information.

- Tapping shifts your energy instead of manipulating your thoughts.

- Tapping is not a magic cure that permanently eliminates anxiety and trauma triggers. It can noticeably reduce anxiety and the intensity of the emotional impact of past experiences that trigger the stress response in the body.

- Sometimes, immediate changes can occur when tapping on a small "t."

- Use FT to break unwanted patterns of thought.

- Tapping can be used before, during, and after a stressful event.

CHAPTER 11

Navigate Life's Stressors with Tapping

Serenity is a choice, not a chance.

So when and what can you use Tapping for? The answer is everything!

Tapping tackles stress on multiple fronts, including current anxiety, potential future concerns, and lingering anxious thoughts from the past. Whether facing minor or major issues, this technique disrupts the automatic stress response; it ushers in a sense of calm and reawakens the Thinking Brain.

Now, consider this: when do you most desire clarity of thought? For me, the answer is unequivocally always. Whether contemplating the future, reminiscing about the past, or dealing with present challenges, I want all mental gears to be fully engaged and firing on all cylinders.

Current Stress, Anxiety, and Frustration

Is there something bothering you that keeps occupying your thoughts? Are you experiencing stress due to everyday annoyances? Tapping helps you process and approach them from a more calm and clear perspective. These concerns don't have to be steeped in something tragic, like an illness. It can be a conflict you are having with someone else. Maybe it's just a minor frustration, like sitting in traffic or waiting on hold with customer service. Are you at the dentist, receiving medical treatment, or looking at your credit card bill? During my divorce when I was depressed and struggling with anxiety, little things riled me. So, I incorporated Tapping more often to maintain my emotional balance and stability.

Tapping is a mind-clearing tool.
When in doubt, Tap and Talk.

Future Stress and Anxiety

You can use Tapping for future stress, or, as we call it in the Tapping vernacular, anticipatory anxiety. These worries are ones that may or may not occur in the future, but you're investing some serious energy to keep them alive. For example: will you receive a good evaluation from your supervisor, will your rent check bounce, will that cute guy really call you, is that mole suspicious, and so on?

No matter what you are ruminating on that is causing you unwanted anxiety, enlist FT to lower your stress because bad feelings don't produce good results. Have you ever heard someone say, "I had an excellent, productive day because I was so stressed out thinking about what may happen next week?" Probably not.

"Life is a matter of choices, and every choice you make makes you." —John C. Maxwell

Tapping for Anticipatory Anxiety: A Domestic Violence Scenario

Disconnecting from future stress to allow for clear thinking can be a matter of life and death. I learned this while working with victims of domestic violence at a support group in Florida. One of the key protocols for domestic violence safety is for the victim to remain calm and be aware of their environment and safety options. It's a survival need.

Under stress, a thoughtfully established safety plan may be ignored or forgotten during a perpetrator's violent outburst. Since every second counts, clear, rational thinking can be the difference between life and death.

My goal was to teach the women how to use FT for anticipatory stress. Many of them were anxious throughout the day, waiting for the abuser to come home, not knowing what mood he would be in. Their consuming fear infringed on their ability to be fully present with their jobs, children, and daily responsibilities. The thought "What will he be like when he gets home?" was ever-present in their minds.

Tapping whenever they felt anxiety throughout the day helped them keep their resourceful, rational minds available. Their lives depended on their ability to respond with clarity instead of reacting out of fear. One survivor said the second she heard the garage door go up, her stomach would drop and her panic would swell. Sometimes, it was a false alarm, only her children returning from school. She imagined putting a warning bell on the garage door that only alerted her when her husband's car pulled into the driveway so she wouldn't panic for no reason.

Another woman shared that her husband was most violent when he drank. Some people have eagle eyes; she claimed she had the ears of a fox. She knew if he was intoxicated by how hard he closed his car door and the sound his shoes made walking up the wooden steps to their side door. She would chastise her children when she was alerted to the dreaded car door slam and foot thumping on the steps. "Dad is in a bad mood, so be quiet and behave." This was code for, "Be alert for an outburst from Dad, and be ready to run." She explained to me, "It's an exhausting way to live. Everyone is always on edge around dinner time."

As the onion was peeled back in this Tapping session, I also heard how fear robbed her of serenity, which cheated the children out of a fully present mother who could address their needs—the mother's guilt ensued. This is a double tragedy. Here she was dealing with domestic abuse while also putting herself down because she wasn't winning the Mother of the Year award. In addition to using FT to help her remain grounded, I taught her how to use STM to relieve her guilt and shame.

Tapping helps you be present for your children by being present for yourself.

Using Tapping for Anticipatory Anxiety Surrounding a Family Reunion

A woman from this support group brought up a scenario that presented her with nine months of daily anxiety because of the sexual abuse she experienced as a child. This anxiety is not because she was being exposed to the perpetrator daily. Her anxiety is an example of a future fear causing daily panic because she knew she would have to face the abuser at a family reunion. Even though she wasn't around the offender physically, her body's nervous system had him on its radar, chirping out anxiety alerts like a frequent storm warning from the National Weather Service.

The woman explained that she would feel a rush of nausea every time she saw interactions on the family reunion Facebook page. An event that wouldn't occur for nine more months was creating daily tremors. Think of the effect on her health! She was dumping harmful stress hormones into her body all day, not to mention she was distracted from life.

She said, "I feel bad because it takes me a while to recenter after I go on Facebook or get notifications from the out-of-town family. I'm not there for my daughters. The rape is still robbing me of my serenity twenty years later! It's so unfair that my children pay for something that happened to me so long ago."

I gave her homework. I told her to Functional Tap to interrupt all her anxious thoughts regarding the reunion—*every* time one arose. She was to Tap, Talk, and Tell the truth. And yes, she may be Tapping on and off all day long. This type of Tapping probably won't offer complete trauma relief; however, her body may relax its hypervigilance over time and believe she is an adult and this person can't harm her anymore.

Think back to neuroplasticity and how we can change the structures of our brains. If this woman Tapped whenever she thought about the upcoming reunion, she would eventually loosen the trauma connection to this event. It wouldn't wholly disappear without her also doing trauma therapy; however, from past experience with my clients, I have found that constantly interrupting anxiety thoughts lessens their intensity and frequency. She may continue to get triggered when she thinks about the reunion, but the level of discomfort on the SUD scale may not be a ten anymore. It might drop to a five.

Tapping for Thoughts of the Past

Does a thought about something from your past ever flash into your consciousness? Not a trauma but some inconsequential experience that, when you think about it, you get angry, sad, hurt, or some other unwanted feeling?

We are told not to sweat the small stuff. But sometimes, I find myself tripping over life's pebbles more than I fret about the mountains. If one of these annoying thoughts crosses my mind a second time, I consider it stuck in my psyche and taking up space. I do FT to snuff out the negative sensations, and if they don't go away, it's an indicator that I need to delve deeper using STM.

We are our memories.

Trifecta Tapping: Past, Present, and Future Anxiety and Stress

You can use Tapping for past, present, or future stress and anxious thoughts. This is what I call "Trifecta Tapping." Your winnings include calmness, presence, clarity, and choices. Remember, this is what I suggested to the foster child's mother who became anxious during extended car rides.

At one point, I taught Trifecta Tapping to women who were court-ordered to attend residential substance-abuse recovery. Some women were anxious about going to court, while others were anxious about a weekly event called "family time." Family time was when they were permitted to have family members visit. These women would experience fear and anxiety before, during, and after the event, so I suggested Trifecta Tapping.

Trifecta Tapping can also be used by professionals. Burnout is causing staggering turnover in many fields, but especially alarming are the statistics surrounding turnover for social workers, educators, early childhood educators, and first responders. It would be a shame if they quit what they love doing because of stress.

When I train child welfare workers and caregivers, one of the learning objectives is that they will be able to lower their anxiety and be fully functional (all minds on deck!) before, during, and after a client home visit (or court appearance or other anxiety event).

Case Study: Anxiety-Inducing Little Girls

While training at a social worker conference in California, I asked for a volunteer to demonstrate how to Tap on anticipatory anxiety. George, who taught social workers at a local university, offered to be the volunteer. In addition to being an educator, George worked in private practice as a social worker for children. He presented an issue of anticipatory anxiety, a.k.a. "dread in advance," but instead, he won big by discovering two trauma themes and a secondary aspect!

George's issue was with a four-year-old client we'll call MiMi. He described how this little "blonde hair, blue-eyed girl" (his words) would often become highly agitated during counseling sessions. "Inevitably, she would fling herself on the floor and commence flapping her arms and legs on the ground, whining."

For some reason that he could not understand, her behavior caused him to become anxious. "I have four children of my own, and I'm one of five children, so being around kids with different personalities and temper tantrums shouldn't throw me into a panic. I've been doing this for thirty years, so this behavior isn't anything new to me."

I asked George about his anxiety surrounding MiMi. While tapping, George explained he had a standing Monday morning appointment with MiMi. He shared that he sometimes had a heavy, somewhat troubling feeling in his gut that lingered throughout the day on the Sunday preceding the visit. Recently, he realized it was caused by the looming Monday morning appointment with MiMi (anticipatory anxiety).

"I've worked with this behavior before, but this little 'blondie' triggers me when she throws herself on the floor and tosses around. I get anxious and stumble through the session, watching the clock the whole time, waiting for the appointment to be over. Honestly, it takes concentrated breathing and serious willpower to stay focused. Now that I think about it, it's embarrassing to say it out loud. I recently talked to the agency director to possibly remove her from my caseload, but that would add more stress to her life so I don't want to do that to her. I just don't understand my overreaction. It's ridiculous." Then he laughed with a bit of unease and said, "I'm never like this."

(Hint: his anxiety makes no sense.)

DISCOVERY INTERVIEW USING THE STM DOCUMENT

For this role-play, I asked for another volunteer to lead George through the Tapping Rounds, once I had led him through the discovery questions.

George's dilemma: I am struggling with the anxiety I experience with MiMi.

Below are the details from the STM document I considered most relevant to use in the Tapping Script:

- "I'm anxious Sunday nights."

- "I feel a dull, dreading feeling in my stomach."

- "I can't manage this four-year-old."

- "It's up to me to stay in control."

- "It's expected of me as the adult."

- "I have a fear that things will get out of control." (Hint: what could that mean since she's tiny and he's an adult male? I spy a past trauma/safety issue.)

- "I am always stressed before my appointments with her." (Hint: Some kind of trigger.)

- "I have so much anxiety."

- "What gives?" (I spy shame/guilt.)

- "Maybe I'm just burned out, and it's time to find a new career." (Flight.)

Before I go any further, let me ask, do you think George has anxiety, fear, or guilt/shame? If you look back at the phrases I gathered from him, it appears he has all of them. Since he presented with anxiety, we continued to use that as our starting aspect because Tapping is the *I-Spy* game—sooner or later, you will uncover the true core feeling.

Then, we had George identify his target emotion and locate where he felt anxiety in his body.

Next, we made a Target Statement: "When I think of my session with MiMi, I feel anxiety in my stomach."

And then we established a SUD score .

I said, "George, close your eyes, go into your body, while tapping, and say, 'When I think of my sessions with MiMi, I feel anxious.' On a scale of one to ten, George, how high is your anxiety when you think of your meetings with MiMi?" Sometimes it's hard to elicit an accurate SUD number when a person is trying to recreate the unwanted sensations or it's not a situational problem like Robyn's panic attacks were. It also makes it incredibly challenging to capture an accurate read while standing in front of a couple hundred of your peers!

George: "Well, it only feels like a five right now, but I would say that typically on Sundays, I only feel a dull sensation of dread for my Monday meeting with MiMi. I would guess that right before the meeting, it may jump to seven or eight. My anxiety during the meeting depends on her mood when she enters the room."

After he said this, he turned to everyone in the room and said, "And please don't judge me. I don't usually react like this."

I turned to the group and asked, "Is he the only person in this room who struggles with a specific client, or do any of you have similar challenges?" Many raised their hands. I turned to George and said, "You are not alone. And I thank you for being courageous, honest, and vulnerable. It will be worth it because you may be able to clear up this difficulty—for good."

Then, I turned the demonstration over to the volunteer, who led him through Tapping Rounds by repeating the words and phrases gathered from the STM document. George echoed them.

Since George was Tapping in front of the room, I could tell he was self-conscious and wasn't experiencing much emotional connection to his body. So, I asked the volunteer to lead him through several more rounds of Tapping. Remember, a Tapping Round is one pass through all eight of the STM points.

The short-term goal of repeating the exact Tapping verbiage was to build his comfort level with the body mechanics of tapping. Ideally, this familiarity with Tapping would settle and lead him more into body presence instead of focusing on getting the tapping mechanics right.

After several Tapping Rounds, we paused, and I asked how he felt. I did not use the SUD score when I asked because he admitted his it wasn't very accurate in the first place. He said he felt a little less anxious but didn't notice much of a shift. At this point, I took over the next series of Tapping and played *I-Spy* to move closer to George's core issue because, at this point, we were on a cold trail. We were looking for some reaction and hadn't received one...yet.

It was time to probe for different aspects of the same problem or a hidden memory. We want to land or poke on a sensitive spot in this *I-Spy* game, so I used a Leading Phrase to see if I could elicit a memory, like with Robyn.

When I took over, I started Tapping with George, using his words from the STM document. Eventually, I slipped in a Leading Phrase.

I did this because even though we were Tapping for anticipatory anxiety, I knew there was a hidden trauma, either big or small, driving this behavior. How? Because it didn't make sense for him to become stressed with only this specific client, just like it didn't make sense for Robyn, a senior-level executive, to panic when the doors closed during a meeting.

What happened next was fascinating. I love the ability of Tapping to bore straight to the core issue!

These are the words I stated first, and he repeated:

- "I'm anxious Sunday nights."

- "I am always stressed before my sessions with her."

- "I have so much anxiety."

- "I feel a dreaded sick feeling in my stomach."

- "My stomach is giving me a message."

- "I can't control this 'blondie.'"

- "And that frightens me."

- "It's up to me to stay in control."

- "It's expected of me as the adult."

- "I have a fear that things will get out of control."

Now, I repeated his last statement and added a few of my leading words. My Leading Phrases are bolded.

"I have a fear that things will get out of control. **And I must control blondie because if I'm not in control of the situation, then...**"

George repeats my exact words.

"I have a fear that things will get out of control. **And I have to control blondie because if I'm not in control of the situation, then...**"

At this point, he paused but didn't finish the statement. Instead, he opened his eyes and looked at me confused—yet he never stopped tapping. I could tell by the shift in his eyes that he felt something, so I poked and repeated the same sentence with the leading phrase.

And George repeated it.

"I have a fear that things will get out of control. **I must stay in control because...**"

Again, he didn't finish the statement, but I could tell his body was starting to remember. However, the experience hadn't surfaced into his conscious memory, so neither had the language. I tried another nudge.

"If I don't keep her under control, then..."

George repeats my exact words.

"If I don't keep her under control, then..."

He looked up at me with wide-eyed shock and tears began welling in his eyes. He whispered, "I can't believe it! It has nothing to do with MiMi."

The body is telling you something.
Are you listening?

It's important to understand that this instant connection doesn't always happen, even if you are a seasoned EFT practitioner like me. Sometimes, however, it takes days or weeks for a memory to rise and a linkage to occur. The cork can pop off the champagne bottle with alarming speed or take weeks to slowly work itself off. People have contacted me weeks after a Tapping session to let me know a memory finally popped up, and a connection was made. "I got it! I know why _____."

We are inherently inclined to make meaning out of experiences. I believe these realizations arise when our unconscious mind senses that we can handle buried painful thoughts. Tapping allows them to emerge safely, enabling us to observe, interpret, and ultimately release them.

GEORGE'S STORY

Like Robyn, George's past trauma created his anxiety surrounding MiMi. While he continued Functional Tapping, he told us his realization. I also asked attendees to tap if they felt any anxiety during his sharing.

"I was the oldest of five children. My mother struggled with bouts of depression, and my dad was an alcoholic. I started being a parent, in a sense, at a very young age. When my dad came home from work, he drank. We knew to stay out of his way and be quiet while he consumed his daily six-pack. As the oldest child, I took it as my responsibility to keep the younger four children quiet and out of his way. I was always on guard to keep us safe. It didn't make for a great childhood because I hardly ever went out and played with other children when my dad was home. I feared that if I left the house, one of my siblings would become loud and rambunctious, as kids do. Then my dad would rage and say they were out of control, and he would become violent. It was terrifying, so for the protection of my siblings, I took it as my parental duty to keep control of the household.

"Depending on how drunk my dad got, he would sometimes push me around more than the others because I slightly stood up to him and protected my siblings. However, I am ashamed to admit that sometimes even I was afraid to get between him and his current victim.

"My youngest sibling is my little sister who we called Chi Chi. She has blonde hair and blue eyes, just like my client MiMi. She was the only one with these features in my family, so we called her 'Little Blondie.'

"Little Blondie was incredibly challenging for me because she always threw fits. I put an exorbitant amount of pressure on myself to watch her and manage her emotions, which is utterly ridiculous because I was just a kid of maybe twelve. But if I didn't, I had to witness the abuse she received from my father. Just talking about it, I can still remember the wild panic in her little blue eyes and the glazed drunken anger in his. The situation was f'ed up. Once I was older, I realized he probably poured more wrath on Chi Chi because she wasn't his biological child. My mother had had an affair, and almost everyone knew it but us kids.

"It sucks that I'm still being affected by this. I went through years of therapy on my childhood issues. I can't believe my toxic childhood is still haunting me. I'm a professional; I know better. Yet I feel so pathetic."

I looked around the room, seeing tears and many knowing nods. I asked the attendees:

"Can anyone identify with a need to be in control resulting from stress and chaos in your childhood home?" There were plenty of nods. Then I said, "How many of you never put this idea of always needing to be in control together with events from your childhood for yourself?" Many more nods.

"Plus, I bet many of you went into the helping field because of your heartache."

Again, nods of agreement.

I turned to George and said, "You are among many who feel the same way you do and have experienced various childhood challenges. Again, George, thank you for your courage to be vulnerable and share."

TRAUMA THEME UNCOVERED—A SERENDIPITOUS GIFT

In the scenario with George, he didn't offer to be a volunteer to address past childhood trauma. He presented an issue of anticipatory anxiety. However, sometimes a past problem arises as the culprit of the anxiety. (Sometimes meaning 99.9 percent of the time.) Like Robyn, he got a BOGO.

Upon further exploration of George's situation, we discovered two themes stemming from his childhood trauma.

The first theme was control: "I must maintain control, or it's not safe."

The other was the same tune with a different chorus—perfectionism: "I must be perfect at all times. If I am perfect, everyone will be safe."

As I briefly described earlier, a theme is an unconscious pattern of thought that pervades one's life and unknowingly influences their behavior. It is typically derived from a juvenile experience where a belief was falsely created and became a limiting constraint on one's life for the faulty purpose of keeping one safe from emotional pain, such as hurt, embarrassment, loss, and abandonment. And, of course, the current safety message influencing one's decisions is probably not even relevant at this point in their life. The brain may be overusing this precautionary message.

GEORGE'S SECONDARY ASPECT: SELF-JUDGMENT

Unfortunately, George's perfectionism led to self-criticism. Like Robyn, George was angry with himself because he wasn't "over" his childhood issues, and his past trauma still affected him. I told George what I tell all my clients: celebrate awareness.

Celebrating is acknowledging and honoring the "knowing" because awareness is the first step to healing painful memories. Simply put, what you know, you can address. Once we have awareness, we can disentangle our past from our present so we no longer need to relive unhealthy patterns that don't serve us. We can embrace life and grow because it is safe to do so.

Your truths will make sense to your body, mind, heart, and soul. Bringing them from the semi-conscious to the conscious is liberating. It can also be terrifying. Make sure you are Tapping while honoring this awareness because it will help you quickly shift the experience from fear or self-loathing to a curious mind of wonder and possibly a smiling celebration.

Borrowing Benefits—When Getting Triggered Is a Good Thing

During any workshop where I do group Tapping, I ask attendees to tap along and inaudibly repeat the phrases, or nearly the same words, as the volunteer client. This is the case no matter whether they can identify with what the client is experiencing and saying or not. If we are Tapping on loss, everyone taps on loss; if it is anger, everyone taps along on rage: ; and if it is perfectionism and control, like George's Tapping topic, that's what they will tap on.

Borrowing Benefits is a Tapping phenomenon where other group attendees may also experience emotions similar to the ones of the volunteer client. This is usually to the surprise of the attendees sitting innocently, Tapping along with the volunteer client, thinking they are immune to what the volunteer is experiencing. Their sensations rise once the body's calm, and something below their awareness connects to the emotion we are Tapping on. Soon, emotions flow. The good news is they also experience the release and peace of Tapping. Depending on the topic we are Tapping on and the workshop attendees, at least a third of the people are usually affected by group Tapping. This is what happened when the group Tapped along with George.

I did a follow-up Tapping session with George on his need for control and perfectionism. Since I encouraged all attendees to Tap along and repeat George's words while I led him through the Tapping, numerous social workers in the audience cried. They didn't cry for George but for their own buried pain. This is Borrowing Benefits.

These attendees didn't "catch" what George was feeling. It is simply a matter of many of us having the same pain in a different disguise. The words we repeated aloud were his words but evoked similar emotions. The participants experienced Borrowing Benefits because they benefited from another's Tapping.

I wanted George to understand how others benefitted from his sharing, so I asked the attendees if they would share their words and phrases that arose from the Tapping session. The emotional essence they shared was similar to George's theme of not feeling safe in his childhood home. Also similar was the need to remain on guard and in control.

This is a partial list of thoughts that arose among the other attendees triggered by George's Tapping session:

- It wasn't safe in my home.

- Be good or else.

- I must remain alert.

- I must be hypervigilant.

- I must always be in control.

- It's my job to be in control.

- Stay in control so outsiders don't know about your family's secret.

- Take charge so the family can function.

- I must be perfect.

Other thoughts expressed were: run, get away, hide, be quiet, and lie.

Some attendees explained how, in their childhood home, instead of staying in control, they shut down and froze. Others just numbed out to avoid the anxiety and pain. Remember, there is a payoff to all behavior. Following that premise, it is essential to understand that in some homes, these behaviors and skills are invaluable to a child and their need to feel safe. However, they may not serve us as adults. Though they were once considered necessary, now these beliefs and behaviors should be examined through adult eyes.

Borrowing Benefits is especially effective when you Tap with groups of people from a specific population, like people struggling with substance abuse, victims of violence, and victims of natural disasters, because they often experience similar beliefs, thoughts, and emotions.

For example, when I work with groups of people with addictions, I always Tap on various attitudes and emotions, especially blame, shame, and anxiety around using again. I have found that these are universal among most addicts. For this reason, group Tapping on these topics is efficient and cost-effective.

It's a Wrap

In George's situation, a one-time Tapping session would not erase the effects of years of developmental trauma. Since George was determined to move on from his childhood trauma, he continued using Tapping after the seminar.

At one point, he emailed me, elated with the results of using the Tapping Trifecta. He was able to lower his anxiety before his sessions with MiMi. He also FT during the sessions to aid in thinking clearly. Then, he Tapped after the sessions when he felt slightly self-critical of his inability to handle the situation "perfectly."

Over time, his anxiety and self-judgment lessened, and he managed the sessions with more confidence and attention, focusing on MiMi's needs instead of controlling his anxiety.

Be kind to yourself because
being human isn't a character defect.

☞ Key Concepts

- Tapping can be used to address current stress, future stress, stress emanating from the past, and both minor and major issues.

- Trifecta Tapping helps mitigate current, future, and past stress. It is a valuable tool for mental health workers, educators, and first responders to increase resiliency while decreasing burnout.

- Using the Leading Phrase technique helps uncover buried emotions, beliefs, and distressing events.

- Group Tapping offers a unique opportunity to help many people at once with Borrowing Benefits.

CHAPTER 12

Solo Tapping and
Other Techniques

*"My imperfections and failures are as much a
blessing from God as my successes and talents, and
I lay them both at his feet." —Mahatma Gandhi*

Sometimes, when the inner panic alarm is sounding, and you don't want to burden your friends with your problem or the earliest appointment with your therapist is three weeks away, you can take matters into your own hands. Literally.

Imagine this scenario. Once again, a particular person at the office didn't do their part, which creates more work for you. Even worse, the person is your superior. Your annoyance increases because dealing with conflict isn't your strength. However, you recently attended one of my Tapping trainings and were inspired not to let this negative energy drag you down, so you decided to Tap.

Here's what I would do. I would go into my office and do the 3Ts audibly or inaudibly. If you don't have a private office, you can go into the bathroom to Tap. (Bathroom Tapping! I think I just coined a new Tapping name!)

Side note: bathroom Tapping is invaluable at the holiday family gatherings that some call "dysfunction junction." (Mom, if you are reading this, don't feel bad; I don't mean us. I mean those other people. We are a completely normal family.)

Continuing with the example of frustrated employee, I would Tap with the aim of relieving my negative energy so I could go on with my workday with clarity (so important), ease, and as much joy as possible. I wouldn't do STM because I don't have time, and I don't want to become emotional at work. I simply want to function.

In the hypothetical dialogue below, you will notice I am Talking and Telling the truth while Tapping (3Ts). It includes recounting the situation and labeling the emotions surrounding the issue that I feel viscerally.

I am answering this statement either audibly or inaudibly: "I feel _____(emotion) because_____ (state the vital details of the problem)."

Before you read the Tapping verbiage below, please think of a situation in your life where you are the one who always goes the extra mile or is expected to do something. A time where you constantly "Suck it up, buttercup," and do it with a smile. This could be in your marriage, with a specific family member, friend, or at work.

Now, while you read the script below, replace my above work story with your story, and see if anything resonates with you. In other words, maybe you could gain some Borrowing Benefits from my hypothetical tale.

Labeling Emotions and Details

- "I am so angry that I am stuck handling other peoples' problems (or instead, include your situation here)."

- "I can't believe she did it again."

- "It drives me crazy."

- "She always does this and then leaves it for me."

- "Then I have to take care of _____."

- "This makes me so angry."

- "Why me?"

- "Why doesn't someone else step up and take care of it?"

- "I'm always the one who is inconvenienced and expected to take care of it."

- "I don't mind stepping up sometimes, but it seems that if I don't do it, no one will."

- "Don't people see this problem?"

- "Or am I the only one who sees this?"

- "It just doesn't seem fair."

- "It's never going to change."

- "This job is exhausting!"

The venting may go on and on, culminating with the following: "And I don't get paid enough for this stress."

As you can see from the above dialogue, I am doing the 3Ts. I am Tapping while expressing my emotions (anger, injustice, exhaustion) and the details (it happened again, I always do it, I don't get paid enough).

When Venting Isn't Enough: Rant Tapping

Master Tapping coach Marti Murphy coined the phrase "Rant Tapping." It is a raging version of vent Tapping. It is used when simple sharing or venting is not an adequate expression of your intense feelings.

Rant Tapping can entail yelling, acting out how you would tell a person off, cursing (if you swear), and possibly crying. Rant Tapping is an exhilarating and cathartic experience. Usually, a person slumps from exhaustion with a full glow afterward. As Marty puts it, "Rant Tapping is freaking unbelievable." And Marty is so right.

I Am Done Purging My Emotions, So What's Next?

Let's continue with the above example of Solo Tapping. After several rounds of Tapping, Talking, and Telling the truth (3Ts), I have let the angst go and feel calmer. If this is the case, I can exit the bathroom with a clear head and peaceful smile, which may appear awkward if someone sees me.

On the other hand, let's say I'm not entirely over my feelings. I am still a little angry, but I must get out of the bathroom and back to work or my ten-hour day will grind even longer. In this situation, it's not that FT didn't work. There are several reasons why my negative emotions may not have dissipated. However, I don't have time to dig deeper into this dilemma with STM. Right now, I want to leave the bathroom feeling less angry.

Dump It and Pivot to Positivity with Happy Tapping

Happy Tapping (another name I dreamed up) is what I call tapping to consciously shift to a more joyful energy. It is the process of dumping negative verbiage and pivoting to neutral, positive, or hopeful language.

In the "Dump It" section of the STM document, I list positive pivoting phrases to help you dump the negative energy and pivot to positive vibes. I will outline below other techniques for this deliberate shift to positive energy. Typically, you Tap until the negative charge naturally dissipates. However, with Happy Tapping, you are making a concerted and strategic effort to create a shift in energy. Many of us already implement means to create positive thoughts and vibes in our lives, like gratitude and affirmation lists. You could also easily add Tapping to these and other positive motivational strategies.

Pivot and Reframe

Calming the emotional brain and its barrage of negative thoughts opens a space for a glimpse of a different perspective and a possible reframing from negativity. This shift to more rational, mature, and positive thoughts often naturally occurs for people who have been Tapping for a while—without attempting to manifest them.

Our bodies and thought processes become conditioned through regular Tapping to effortlessly reframe the situation and shift to wonder positivity, or acknowledgment of our humanness. If this moving and reframing process isn't occurring for you as a beginner, I would suggest Tapping with a professional. You could also use positive pivoting phrases to encourage the shift or create your own list of affirmations before you begin Tapping. Some examples are: "I choose to release this now;" "I choose to be calm and peaceful;" and "I'm okay right now."

Use Self-Praise and Tapping to Pivot

Another way to ramp up the good vibes and endorphins is by Tapping on statements of self-praise. If you or your client are struggling with creating a self-praise list, create one together or ask friends and family for input. It could be homework for a client to be brought back to the next counseling session.

Tapping Gratitude and Affirmations to Pivot

Many of us turn to affirmations or a gratitude list to consciously focus on the good things in our lives instead of the bad. You can express gratitude while Tapping. The gratitude list can relate to your current distress, but it doesn't have to. It is simply a mechanism to lead you away from angst to a place of warmer energy—even if only temporarily.

POSITIVE PIVOTING PHRASES

"Words have to have integrity for them to stick."
—Martha Beck

Below are a few positive pivoting phrases. Create your own and include affirmations. The key is that they must resonate with how you feel now, not what you want to feel in the future.

- "These are my feelings right now, just for this minute."

- "This is only a part of how I feel."

- "I am allowed to have these thoughts because I am human, and this is part of the human condition."

- "I am not God (Buddha, Mother Teresa, Gandhi, Jesus); I am an earthly person."

- "I made a mistake; I'm not a mistake."

- "I didn't raise myself to be like this."

- "Considering where I came from, I would likely react like this. It's a natural human reaction from a person who went through what I went through. It's funny to think that I wouldn't react like this. I would have to be made of stone not to have these feelings."

- "Yes, I wish I had the love and ability to forgive like (God, Buddha, Mother Teresa, Gandhi, Jesus), but alas, I haven't self-actualized yet." (FYI: humor is an excellent way to reframe.)

- "My feelings don't say anything about who I am. They only say that I am human."

- "Only a part of me feels this way; only a tiny, 10 percent (pick a percent) part of me feels this way."

- "Who I am at this moment is not who I am all the time."

- "I permit myself to not be perfect."

- "What if I could accept this part of me?"

- "What if I could love, or at least not put down, this part of me?"

- "What if I wrap my arms around this part of me and say, 'I know that you are struggling, and I honor your efforts.'"

- "I choose to release this_____ (name the emotion) now."

- "I choose to be kind, patient, and understanding to myself like I would be to a friend because being human isn't a character defect."

- "I profoundly love and accept all of me."

- "I am not perfect, but parts of me are exceptional."

If your mind or body pushes back while Tapping and disagrees with one of these phrases, this is also valuable information. It indicates you may need to adjust your statements to resonate authentically and align with what you feel right now.

Below are examples of the gentle shifting verbiage I use when doing group Tapping work with people in recovery. After we have Tapped, admitted the hidden truths, and cried, I attempt to move them a little closer to self-love. I say "attempt" because these women stole from friends and family; were emotionally, physically, and sexually harmed; and possibly lost custody of their children. Even though many of them point to others as the reason for their problems, they also live with a scornful internal judge. Self-love isn't easy for them to embrace.

They repeat my phrases while Tapping as if they were trying shoes on to see if they fit. I don't move through the phrases quickly. If I see many nods, I might repeat a statement several times, tapping all the while.

- "I'm struggling to become my best self."

- "I want to love and praise myself more, but it is hard. It's tough."

- "I can't expect complete self-love and acceptance to happen overnight."

- "I will take time to acknowledge my efforts and trust the process."

- "It takes courage to face my feelings, and I applaud myself for trying."

- "Today, I will speak gently to myself, trusting that self-love will come a little closer to me."

- "I know I am not perfect, but I am trying."

- "What if I could accept myself a tiny bit more?"

- "What if I could find a couple of things I am doing right?"

- "I understand this is a process, and I am open to allowing more peace and self-love into my life."

- "It is safe to love a part of me."

- "I am beginning a journey to love all of me."

- "Just for today, I will look for good things about myself, no matter how small."

- "When I begin to accept myself exactly as I am, life will feel more serene."

If you noticed, I designed my phrases to open the person to the possibilities of self-love. I didn't jump to unrealistic accolades like, "Even though I stole from my grandmother, I am a good person." Kind words that don't fit don't stick. In fact, fabricated praise may cause a person to push back and say, "Oh no. I suck, and I am not a good person." They push back attempting to persuade you of how bad they are instead of moving toward self-love. This is all pertinent information to explore and address.

Try on affirmations and attitudinal adjustment techniques like you are trying on shoes to see which ones will fit best for a long night of standing at a wedding reception. You try them on, walk around, and see how they feel. If they fit, they will stick!

Pivot with Argue Tapping

Argue Tapping is one of my favorite pivoting techniques. You don't argue in a mean voice or aggressively. Instead, you debate both sides of the dilemma with yourself.

You Tap on a negative thought or phrase and then immediately follow it with a positive one.

Argue Tapping trains the brain to replace a negative with a positive. This continual back-and-forth short circuits neural pathways and trains the brain to think differently. Eventually, you automatically hear the positive thought when you feel the negative one. It also creates doubt in the validity of your negative narrative. This allows an opening for other possibilities.

Here's a simple example:

"I probably won't get the job because _____."

"Maybe I will."

"I know I won't."

"There is a possibility I will get it."

"It will never happen."

"I am not God/the universe. I don't know everything."

Here's another example:

"I could never leave my husband because _____."

"Maybe I could."

"No, I could never leave him."

"A part of me believes I could."

"No, I couldn't."

"Perhaps I could at some point."

With Argue Tapping, you aren't trying to convince yourself of anything. Instead, the process inhibits negative feedback loops and encourages your brain to think differently. It's like tricking your brain so that eventually when you hear the negative thought, you automatically hear the positive one too.

Going to extremes is sometimes effective to lighten the mood and break a negative thought process.

"I should have never done what I did."

"It's OK. You didn't mean to do what you did."

"No, I am the worst mother."

"Really? Are you the worst mother in the world? The worst mother in all of history?"

Public Tapping Technique: Not Saying Anything At All

Tapping while in public can be challenging. It would be incredibly awkward to begin Tapping while standing in front of the very person triggering you. It doesn't ease the conflict or help the relationship. That's why I invented something I call "Public Tapping."

Public Tapping isn't Tapping at all. It is an imperceptible on-and-off pressure on EFT meridian points without saying anything out loud.

Our bodies sense what we feel, so it isn't vital to verbally state it. For example, if you see two people physically fighting in a parking lot, do you need to announce how you feel? Or does your body already know? Public Tapping assists you in remaining calm and clear while in public.

I invented it by incorporating meridian points from traditional EFT. You can use the ones I created or invent your own. Remember, you inconspicuously press sensitive meridian points to interrupt anxiety and induce calm.

If you are more of a visual learner, go to my YouTube Channel "Tijana Coso" for a video demonstration.

SIDE OF THE EYE (ONE OR TWO HANDS)

Imagine being trapped at a large meeting listening to a speaker drone on and thinking about all the work piled on your desk or personal matters that need attention. Or, possibly the speaker is addressing a policy or procedure you disagree with, and you're becoming agitated. So you casually lean forward, place one elbow on the table, and rest your chin in the palm of your hand. Your fingertips naturally reach the vicinity of several EFT points on your face: Side of the Eye, Under the Eye, Under the Nose, and Chin.

Rest a fingertip on one of these points and start gently pressing without lifting the finger off of your skin. Voilà! You have interrupted the brain chatter and can remain calm and clear-headed. If the meeting is long and you don't want to seem frozen or bored, you can shift to different face points. You can also nod as if what is being said is fascinating instead of triggering you to fight, flight, or *sleep.*

SIDE OF THE HAND POINT

Drop your hands under the table and press the Side of the Hand point to continue the calming sensation. This also is a great point to use when sitting in your car at stoplights—aka Steering Wheel Tapping.

PINCHING FINGERS

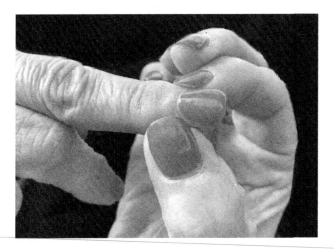

My go-to Public Tapping points are Pinching Fingers and the Gamut Point described below. When pinching my fingers, I squeeze the tip of each finger near the cuticle area, not at the base or middle of the finger. I am not pinching my finger from the top of the fingertip on the nail to the bottom of my finger, where my fingerprint lies. Instead, I am squeezing the finger from side to side at the base of the cuticle. You can perform this any way you prefer. The key is to squeeze on the cuticle area.

You can inconspicuously fold your hands on the top of a table or drop them under the table or desk and pinch them while resting on your lap. Pinch and rotate until you have relief or shift to the Gamut Point.

GAMUT POINT

There is a Tapping technique called the "EFT Nine-Gamut Procedure." It isn't spoken of as much and is even more peculiar-looking than the traditional EFT protocol. While I don't talk about the technique in this book, I do use a Tapping point from the Nine-Gamut technique for Public Tapping. This point is located on the top of your hand—between the bones of the pinky finger and the ring finger. It isn't the webbing between your fingers; it's a bit more toward your wrist.

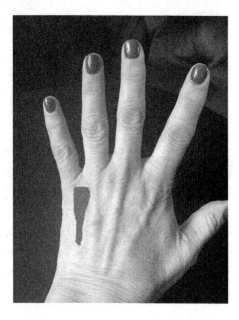

If you look at pictures of me taken while I'm training, I always stand with my hands clasped together. Some say I look like an opera singer ready to launch into an aria. I'm actually Public Tapping on the Gamut Point!

I don't do this because I am fearful or anxious. I love training. I do this to keep myself on task and focused by ensuring the prefrontal Thinking Brain is idling and ready to roll. I always want to show up as the best version of myself.

When I have a highly emotional client or one crying on and off, I suggest they stop moving through Tapping points. Instead, I suggest they lower their hands to their lap and switch to Side of the Hand, Pinching Fingers, or Gamut Point Tapping because that is more comfortable than circling through all of the meridian points.

☞ Key Concepts

- Tapping is expressing with words what you think and feel within your mind and your body while tapping on acupuncture meridian points.

- When you want to shift from negative energy to positive energy, pivot away from the negative by using Happy Tapping, reframing the perspective.

- If, while Tapping, your mind and body don't agree with positive statements, this may indicate you need to adjust your statements so they register as authentic and align with what you feel at this very moment.

- Use Argue Tapping to change your perspective and break negative thinking patterns.

- When you're in public and can't talk out loud, try Public Tapping.

CHAPTER 13

Tapping on Negativity

Tapping helps neutralize reactive patterns,
breaking harmful feedback loops.

People use Tapping to address stress, anxiety, and trauma. None of these are positive topics. Acknowledging negative and painful truths is challenging because, typically, no one wants to sit in their poo and talk about it. Unless, of course, you're a two-year-old.

However, the foundation of Tapping is addressing the pain before shifting to pleasure. Louise Hayes, a motivational author, compares handling the negative messages before switching to positive thoughts to putting groceries away. Clean out unwanted and rotten food in the refrigerator before adding new items. Clean out the old to make way for the new.

What Tapping Is Not

The process of Tapping isn't meant to encourage you to become a Debbie Downer and ruminate on how horrible something is. You only need to stay in the moment of your distress for as long as you need to process the unwanted emotions you are currently experiencing. Plus, the calming nature of Tapping puts some emotional distance between you and your negative ideas. Then, as the drawbridge door opens and your insight improves, you can effortlessly transition to clarity, reframed possibilities, and even positive thoughts.

When stating your negative thoughts while Tapping, I am not suggesting you celebrate them and say things like, "Hooray! I hate my job," "Yippee! I am going through a divorce," or "Thank God! I have fibromyalgia."

Speaking the truth is integrity, and our body knows this. If the truth is negative, it is negative. If it doesn't represent the person we want to be, it's information. Even if it's information you don't want to know about at the conscious level, it's impacting you anyway. In essence, you are discovering truths while seeking to incrementally shift them toward change and positivity.

It feels counterintuitive, but telling the truth is not meant to harm us. It is intended to set us free. The sooner we accept the current reality, the sooner we can change it.

In the early years of EFT, practitioners never Tapped on positive words and thoughts. It wasn't until the last couple of decades, with the rise in the popularity of positive psychology, that EFT practitioners began to add positive verbiage to the Tapping Script.

Why Tap on the Negative?

Experienced EFT practitioners understand that positive Tapping, or what I call "Happy Tapping," is only a temporary Band-Aid. It is used to stave off the unwanted emotions that eventually resurface into awareness or remain below the surface like an ocean's undertow, continually pulling a person away from their destination—goals, passions, personal values. Unless you remove the core issues with STM or traditional EFT, the person will be triggered again.

Research suggests that things like gratitude lists, affirmations, and other means to shift our emotional states are only temporary fixes, like duct tape. In fact, according to the Acceptance and Commitment Theory (ACT) and studies surrounding thought suppression, affirmations and other methods for emotional modification are most effective when things are going well in one's life, not when a person is in the dumps.8 The wave of positive psychology created a toxic backwash called "Toxic Positivity." This concept also suggests that denying emotions can be harmful.9

Trauma and Negative Talk

If you struggle with speaking about the negative and your inner pain, consider current trauma research. Part of trauma recovery is becoming aware of these unwanted emotions, acknowledging them, and, as van der Kolk suggests, befriending and accepting them. There is, of course, significantly more required for effective and complete trauma recovery. The current trauma protocol of identifying, feeling, and accepting the inner pain is similar to telling the truth while Tapping. Putting one's feelings into words with Tapping helps a person downregulate and dissolve their emotional impact.

What does van der Kolk mean when he says "Becoming aware of our inner experience" or "To befriend what is going on inside ourselves"? I can tell you what he doesn't mean. He doesn't mean denying and burying those negative thoughts and experiences or creating affirmations, gratitude lists, or a happy vision board. Or

8 Wegner et al., "Paradoxical Effects of Thought Suppression."; Steven C. Hayes and Spencer Smith, *Get Out of Your Mind and Into Your Life: The New Acceptance and Commitment Therapy (A New Harbinger Self-Help Workbook)* (Oakland, CA: New Harbinger Publications, 2005).

9 Benjamin P. Chapman et al., "Emotion Suppression and Mortality Risk over a 12-Year Follow-Up," *Journal of Psychosomatic Research* 75, no. 4 (October 2013): 381–385, https://doi.org/10.1016/j.jpsychores.2013.07.014.

turning to maladaptive coping tools to pretend the negative experiences don't exist.

I tell my trainees to get the junk out of the trunk. For example, have you ever forgotten you left something like a metal water bottle in the trunk? With every turn, it rolls and makes a banging noise. You want to pull over to secure it or get it out of the trunk, but you are too busy to stop.

This happens in life when you bury or try to distract yourself from unfavorable memories and traumas big and small. The junk in the trunk does not go away. This constant banging reminds you of what you don't want to think about. Several theories suggest that thought suppression causes a rebound effect.[10] The very nature of trying not to think about what you don't want to think about causes you to think about it!

> *You can't jump over pain to get to pleasure.*
> *But you can Tap to create a calm path to get to the*
> *other side.*

Remember, all emotions and feelings are fluid messages that come and go. These messages aren't facts and don't represent who we are. They only reflect what we are feeling right at this moment.

If you have been around a toddler experiencing a temper tantrum, you have witnessed this fluidity of feelings. One minute, they might try to hit you and say you are mean and they hate you, and then, not even five minutes later, they want to sit in your lap and have you read them a book.

---

[10] Wegner et al., "Paradoxical Effects of Thought Suppression."

Will Tapping on the Negative Make Me Negative?

Even with the research, I continue to have concerns from people who pride themselves on always being positive.

"I'm afraid if I talk negatively, I might make myself feel worse."

"I am a positive person, and I don't like to be negative."

"I am not a victim, so I don't want to speak like one."

I understand. Believing that good things will happen if we concentrate on negative thoughts is counterintuitive. This concept flies in the face of one of my favorite phrases, "Thoughts that fire together, wire together." So, you probably wonder if you think negative thoughts, won't they wire together?

I would never suggest that people constantly think and speak negatively. I don't walk around spewing negativity. Tapping while thinking negative thoughts presents opposing sensations. One fear-based feeling and another that is soothing. They collapse each other, and then, from a place of safety, the drawbridge goes down; your calm clarity allows you to respond with your Thinking Brain instead of reacting from fear.

With Tapping, it's not about ruminating on horrible feelings. It's about acknowledging and moving through them by connecting, reflecting, and reframing. It's about dissipating the negative charge to bring the Thinking Brain back online.

Self-Judgment

Turning inward and looking at your honest feelings may cause you to be vulnerable or even self-critical. Tapping eases the Pain

Another concern of stating a negative is what happens when we turn the magnifying glass on ourselves and create self-judgment. We are often the hardest on ourselves.

Even though most of our self-talk is based on half-truths and antiquated stories that we tell ourselves stemming from long-ago experiences, we believe they are fact. And we unknowingly seek confirmation of these untruths, creating an inaccurate documentary of our lives. For example, a person may have a belief or narrative that they aren't smart. Then, when they don't receive a position they seek at work, this becomes their social proof, and they say, "See, I told you I'm not smart enough." When, actually, the decision wasn't based on intelligence but on a different criterion.

Self-judgment is a confession that we don't want to hear, so we push that beach ball down under the water. Some of these critical voices are heard as our own, while others whisper in our ears. They are the filter through which we interpret our life's interactions. Self-judgment is a fast train to a dark place. The negative loop can lead into depression, undermining the hard work you have done on your fabulous self.

I call self-judgment the "committee in your head." Do any of these statements sound familiar to you?

- "Why did I do that again?"
- "Why am I always judging people? I shouldn't judge people."
- "I have no discipline."
- "I will be stuck here forever."
- "I don't deserve a better ____."
- "My parent was right; I will never_____."
- "I am such a phony."
- "I am a bad mother."
- "If they knew what I am really like, they wouldn't like me."

By acknowledging these falsehoods and Tapping on them, we release their power over us. Bessel van der Kolk puts it this way, "As long as you keep secrets and suppress information, you are fundamentally at war with yourself. The critical issue is allowing yourself to know what you know."11

Even though telling the truth about oneself is frightening, Tapping allows a person to examine their thoughts and actions in a calming, understanding, and compassionate space. It's like sharing your deepest secrets with a sympathetic and safe person. The operative word is "safe."

If you continue Tapping on your self-judgment with compassion, you will be less afraid to live in the present and face your hidden beliefs—even ones that point an accusing finger directly at your soul.

The Share-and-Shame Phenomenon

It seems self-judgment arises no matter what topic a person is Tapping on. I call it "sharing and shaming," which occurred with Robyn, George, and even the women experiencing domestic violence.

It seems to be a ubiquitous human condition. Once we acknowledge and attempt to release hidden thoughts we believe aren't socially acceptable, we want to chastise ourselves—share and shame.

For example, a mother uses FT to lower her anger toward her daughter's excessive drinking. Then, her internal judge condemns her for not being a more compassionate mother about her child's current struggles. Martha Beck refers to this cultural restraint as "cultural compliance."12

Remember, feelings aren't facts. They are temporary. When using Tapping, you don't have to fear looking inward and allowing

11 Bessel A. van der Kolk, *The Body Keeps the Score: Brain, Mind, and Body in the Healing of Trauma* (New York: Penguin Books, 2014).

12 Martha Beck, *The Way of Integrity: Finding the Path to Your True Self* (New York: The Open Field/ Penguin Life, 2021).

the inner critic to surface. When you Talk, Tap, and Tell the truth, you are not chastising and apportioning blame for your "human condition." You simply are meeting yourself where you are at this moment.

In the example above, with the mother regretting her honest anger, she would FT acknowledging both thoughts: "She is struggling, and so am I."

If you begin shaming yourself, I suggest you Functional Tap to release that beach ball of self-criticism you have struggled to keep submerged. You do this by first acknowledging the truth while Tapping.

Let's continue with this example. Here is what she may say while FT to lessen her shame:

- "I am not necessarily excited and proud of my anger."

- "I hate to admit this because I feel sorry for her, but I am angry about my daughter's alcohol use!"

- "Actually, I'm really ticked off!"

- "Doesn't she see she's going down the same path as her father?"

- "We have spent thousands of dollars on recovery treatments, and she's still using!"

- "I am so angry about this!"

- "What is wrong with her?"

- "And now that she is using again, I have to take care of her children."

- "I dearly love my grandchildren, but I am angry."

- "I resent that I have to raise more children at sixty-six years old."

- (Pause.)

- "And right now, I choose to voice this deep, secret emotion."

At this point, she could keep venting, or she may have started crying. If this person is Solo Tapping, she could continue tapping on each statement until she felt a shift in her body.

Let's assume that, after venting, tears and shame arose.

- "I can't believe I said that about my daughter."
- "She is suffering."
- "I should be more compassionate."
- "I should be more motherly."
- "What's wrong with me?"
- "What kind of mother am I?"

At this point, she may continue to chastise herself for having what she deems unmotherly feelings. If I were Tapping with her, I would first allow her to FT and purge her emotions, including self-judgment, because people often feel better by saying their forbidden emotions aloud.

Usually, they conclude they aren't horrible people, only exhausted, sad, hurt, and fearful. They come around to self-compassion for themselves and compassion for others. However, if she wasn't naturally (from the FT process) shifting to kinder words about herself and softening her self-criticism, I would lead her through some Tapping and insert more neutral and gentler words.

Here are some ways she could pivot to acceptance of the emotions and situation:

- "I'll tell you what type of mother I am."

- "I am a tired mother and grandmother."

- "I have worked hard, and I am exhausted."

- "And I have a right not to be pleased."

- "A part of me is angry, a part of me is resentful, and a part of me is sad."

- "These are only feelings that I am feeling right now."

- "I have a right to my feelings."

- "I will allow myself to have these feelings."

- "I will not stuff them down."

- "They are only temporary feelings."

- "Feelings are fluid, and it is okay to have these feelings."

Looking at the dialogue above, you will see my shift from shame to acceptance; however, I would be watching for signs from this woman. I would look for nods of agreement to see if she purged all of her emotions on each point I stated. You could test this by using the SUD on this topic: "For example, say this out loud and rate your SUD. I have a right to my feelings. On a scale of one to ten, how accurate is that statement, with ten being I have a right to feel how I do and a one being I don't have a right because I am a terrible mother?"

Once the mother has shifted into acceptance, clarity will rise, and choices will be seen.

When you Tap and these beach balls of self-criticism rise, instead of panicking and attempting to keep them submerged, let them pop to the surface. Once they float on the surface, they are seen for what they are—spheres of messages and information. Then, when you have processed them, you can toss them out of the pool and enjoy the sunshine.

You interact with the world differently when you release yourself from the oppression of self-criticism.

Warning, Warning: This Is Vital—Read This No Matter What!

You may believe I am being a little dramatic with the above heading, but the point I am about to make has significantly influenced my life. Just as there is toxic positivity, there is also a toxic habit of self-judgment. So whenever I Tap alone or with a client and allow the inner critic to be heard, I never end a Tapping session with self-judgment. Ever.

This is because the research on the effects of self-criticism is astounding.[13] It doesn't just make change more challenging: it leads to continual suffering. Self-critical people are more susceptible to depression. They build walls and isolate themselves from others.

---

[13] Kristin Neff, *Self-Compassion: The Proven Power of Being Kind to Yourself* (New York: William Morrow, 2015).

It isn't easy to act and achieve your goals when feeling this way. Energy is drained which needs to be used to get back on track or work through hard times.

You're holding yourself back because your emotional brain believes it's too dangerous to change. Even though the intent is to protect, the impact can be self-sabotage. Never, *ever* end Tapping with self-criticism.

☞ Key Concepts

- Trauma research and theories like ACT suggest thought suppression is not an effective strategy for eliminating negative thoughts.

- Studies have found that toxic positivity, affirmations, and other methods for emotional modification are most effective when things are going well in one's life.

- Never end Tapping on self-judgment or shame. Always pivot to positive Tapping.

PART THREE

QUESTIONS AND TROUBLESHOOTING

CHAPTER 14

Frequently Asked Questions (FAQs)

Some Tapping is better than no Tapping.

Below are some of the most common questions I receive at conferences and seminars. Some of them I have already addressed; however, I included them anyway as a refresher and reference point.

Can I Tap Wrong?

When it comes to the physical act of tapping on your body, you can't do it wrong: *it's all good.*

In Chapter Fifteen, I will outline things that impact Tapping's effectiveness. None of them have to do with the mechanical aspects of Tapping. This means you don't have to tap perfectly on some magic spot or get an exact angle or approach to the point.

How Many Fingers Do I Use?

To answer this question, let's return to the analogy of the reflex test doctors perform. Your leg pops up when the doctor taps the rubber mallet on your knee. If you take the side of your hand and use it like a mallet to hit your leg, it will also pop up. The same happens if you use a cell phone instead of a rubber mallet. My point is that when you tap on your body, it doesn't know if you are using a rubber mallet, the side of your hand, or a cell phone (other than it might hurt a bit if you tapped too hard with a mallet or cell phone).

You can gently tap on meridian points with one finger, two fingers, a fist, or a steering wheel. What you use is irrelevant. You simply exert pressure on a meridian point. Tapping on these points automatically induces a bodily response—you Tap, you calm.

Which Side of the Body Should I Tap on? Which Hand Should I Use? Where Do I Start and Stop Tapping?

You can tap on either side of your body, you can use either hand (or any finger(s)), and you can start and finish anywhere. Your body doesn't know the difference. It is a matter of personal preference.

How Hard and Fast Should I Tap?

Tapping hard on your body isn't necessary to elicit a response. Often, I don't tap at all. I press on the meridian points to produce the same calm as tapping, as in the Public Tapping technique. Why? Because it's automatic! You tap, you calm. Do you see a pattern here?

The speed doesn't matter either. However, I find that if I'm angry, I tap faster; if I'm sad, I tap more slowly.

Can You Tap on Another Person?

Yes. I've worked with European EFT practitioners whose protocol is to tap on the person, not have them tap themselves. I have tapped on my clients, such as when I've worked with groups of veterans, female victims of domestic violence, and women with addictions. At some point, they were crying so hard while tapping that I asked them if I could tap on them to help calm and ground them before we continued. We didn't talk at all. I simply tapped on them while they cried. The curious thing is, afterward, they all usually smiled with relief, or, should I say, *because of* the release.

Are There Other Ways to Tap?

I've had clients share with me the various types of body massaging and tapping they did unconsciously and now realize was a form of soothing. I had one client who clicked the top of her pen up and down. The clicking sensation on her thumb, as well as the noise, are what she used to calm herself down during the day. I say if the methods you've developed work for you, do them.

What Do the Effects of Tapping Feel Like?

Of course, this is personal. Some sensations you may experience in your body include a wave of flowing energy, tingling, warmth, yawning, tears, or a cathartic release. If someone says they don't feel anything, this could be for several reasons, which I will address in the next chapter.

Can a Client Have a Cathartic Experience?

When someone goes through a particularly emotionally intense Tapping session, like with therapy, they may have an emotional and physical crash. I don't mean they physically fall off their chair and crash to the floor. They decompress and slump down in their chair like they just ran a marathon, or maybe had the best-ever massage. Dealing with emotional issues can be exhausting, so it makes sense to feel a cathartic release once a particularly emotional problem is Tapped on.

Is Tapping Along with YouTube Videos Helpful?

There are millions of EFT videos on the web, with people demonstrating Tapping on every topic you could imagine. When I say every subject, I'm not joking. In addition to more severe issues, I found EFT videos for decorating a new house, constipation, and adopting pets.

I am often asked if these videos are helpful. I say any Tapping is better than no Tapping. It depends on what you expect to accomplish from watching someone lead you through a Tapping video using words, thoughts, and beliefs that are personal to them and not necessarily to you. There is magic in using your own words when Tapping. When phrases resonate with you, they are more likely to elicit a visceral response. That said, watching videos of others leading Tapping can be beneficial and offer relief. But there is a way to make them even more effective.

I recommend my clients Tap along with EFT videos to help them uncover their golden nugget, meaning they use the video to see what triggers them. For example, if a person has anxiety about a job interview, they could search for EFT videos on this topic. Then, they could tap along to see which specific aspects of the Tapping verbiage being presented are triggering anxiety. Use the videos as an *I-Spy* game to help discover additional triggering factors. Once those aspects are identified, turn the video off and do a STM session using the STM document. Tap on each identified element causing unease.

I Want to Start This at My School, Agency, or Company. How Can I Get Started?

Through the Tapping Project, I am creating several population-specific programs. Check out my website, www.TheTappingProject. com, for more information. Otherwise, when choosing an EFT program, consider what you want to accomplish, the simplicity of the program, retention training, and if you feel a fit with the instructors.

If There Are Several Issues and Emotions, Where Do I Start First?

Start with the aspect that has the most charge—or start wherever you want. Remember, it's all good. Once you work through one issue, you can start on the next. Keep working through each element using STM and the 3As until your SUD score is at your desired level.

Will It Work If I Am Skeptical or Resistant to Tapping?

Yes.

Reasons to Stop Tapping

Here are a few reasons to discontinue Tapping:

- Stop to discover if you are still on the right track (remember the *I-Spy* game). Check to see if the SUD score has lowered or increased.

- Tapping possibly opened a different emotion or aspect. For example, you may have begun Tapping on anger and then another feeling rose, like guilt or sadness. If there is a shift, stop and decide which emotion to follow.

- Your client is crying, and you want to see if they need a break.

Do I Need a Certification to Use or Teach Tapping?

It depends on how and why you will be using Tapping. I had to get certifications for what I wanted to accomplish with Tapping. However, I would consider learning FT if you are using Tapping to reduce anxiety and experience grounding. I specifically created FT to be easily used and taught to others. It is taught in schools and by mental health professionals, school counselors, and caseworkers to work with and teach their clients. If you can teach someone how to do a cleansing breath, you can teach them how to do FT.

If you believe you can teach someone FT and aren't teaching it to them because you don't have a certification, I suggest you use STM to discover why you aren't putting what you learned into practice. What hidden belief or story are you telling yourself that is holding you back?

I Want to Get Certified. Where Do I Start?

There are numerous programs to get certified in Tapping, most of which I can't recommend because I don't know what they entail or what your specific goals are. However, I took courses from Carol Look, Marti Murphy, and Peta Stapleton, and I highly recommend their work. I also offer a Functional Tapping Certificate. Check my website to sign up and receive details (www.functionaltapping.com).

Should I Teach FT to My Kid(s)?

Absolutely yes. If you have seen any of my training videos, you know that one of my life goals is to get Tapping into the hands of children—literally. The best way to do this is to start when they are young and model it for them.

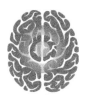

CHAPTER 15

Troubleshooting: What If Tapping Doesn't Work?

Progress, not perfection.

Your Issue Is Too General

Being too general about an issue can hinder its effectiveness. Tapping on low self-esteem or being overwhelmed are topics that aren't specific enough and don't address core emotions. Remember, to win in the *I-Spy* game, you must identify the hot issues and feelings, not the lukewarm ones.

Maybe It Did Work, and You Didn't Notice the Shift

Sometimes, there are instant and profound results with Tapping, like a one-and-done or an enlightening "Aha!" moment. Other times, Tapping loosens ingrained patterns of repetitive thoughts and behaviors, allowing for a minor shift in the psyche. Once the death grip of the limiting belief, fear, or anxiety is loosened, other modalities and therapies become effective. The way I explain it is that Tapping lubricates the nervous system like oil on the gears in a car, allowing shifts to occur smoother and quicker.

With this loosening, several things can occur because, unbeknownst to you, you show up differently. Your interactions change, choices are revealed, and inspired thoughts rise. However, people are often too busy to notice the shift immediately. After a couple of days or weeks, they become aware of a change. They realize they aren't doing the unwanted behavior addressed in the Tapping session, they are moving ahead on something they were procrastinating on, or someone who was triggering them no longer does. Eventually, they notice and say, "Wow, I wonder why?" (Spoiler: it was the Tapping.)

Skill Level of Practitioner

If you're working with a professional and Tapping didn't work, consider the expertise of the practitioner. Tapping is a skill like any other—some practitioners are better than others.

If you're Tapping on yourself with out success, try working with a professional.

Aspects Switched: I Spy a New Subject and Emotion

Problems that aren't alleviated or return after Tapping may indicate different aspects of the original problem that have not yet been cleared. Each one needs to be eliminated before complete and permanent relief can occur.

Safety Litmus Test

If Tapping isn't working, it may be a safety issue. If it's not safe to go into the body and feel your fears or emotions, your unconscious will find a way to block you from feeling and remembering. The innate safety mechanisms used by the brain and body are intelligent and protective. They will keep you emotionally safe until, if, and when you can manage the new information. Tapping does a lot to help you feel safe while exploring issues, but if you don't feel safe with your practitioner or you're trying to Tap in front of someone else that you don't have complete trust with, the process may not work.

Psychological Reversals (Also Called "Secondary Gain" or "Secondary Benefit Syndrome")

If you win, you actually lose—
so it's better to stay stuck.

Having a "secondary benefit" is often why Tapping may not be working. This term, used in the medical and mental health fields, describes a secondary advantage that comes with having a disorder or disease that the patient doesn't want to improve. For example, if a patient on disability improves, they will not receive support payments and must return to work. Thus, it is a secondary benefit to remain ill.

Self-sabotage can occur when the unconscious mind perceives it is better or safer to hold onto a problem. Having a secondary benefit is frequently one of the things I consider when Tapping is not working.

Anxiety is a common problem that has a secondary benefit. By Tapping, clients discover they want to keep their anxiety despite having invested time and money in attempting to eliminate it for various reasons. I've listed some examples below. As you look at the following list, notice that the payoff varies from person to person.

- Anxiety keeps me alert.

- Being worried is being prepared.

- Anxiety keeps me moving and, thus, skinny.

- Anxiety keeps me productive. I would be a slob like my father if I weren't anxious.

- Whom would I be without it?

- If I am not nervous, I will have to do things I don't want to. If I hide behind anxiety, others step forward and take these roles.

- My adult son and his three children won't move in with me if I am highly anxious and unable to handle the change.

Uncovering a secondary benefit with Tapping is an advanced skill and an art. It's like discovering 'who dunnit' in a Sherlock Holmes mystery.

Before the secondary benefit is revealed to them, the client ardently proclaims they want to eliminate their problem: get the job, lose the weight, start a business, rid themselves of anxiety, go back to school, finish the book, find a loving partner, and so on. These are the reasons they are doing Tapping sessions. So, undoubtedly, they want to achieve their goals. Right? Wrong!

Clients are often shocked to discover they are the ones unconsciously blocking or sabotaging something they claim to desire. Often, they have gone to therapy for years only to realize they are inflicting continued pain on themselves. I love watching the mystery being solved and the incredulity unfolding across their faces.

"Wait, you're telling me I am purposely sabotaging my efforts to get the promotion I desperately need and want?"

At this point, I always say, "I'm not telling you anything. Your body told you."

The body is the bridge.

How to Uncover Secondary Benefits

Since this is an advanced skill, I won't go into too much detail in this book; however, I will offer a few suggestions.

One way to know a person has a secondary benefit blocking relief is that their SUD score does not go down or up, even though they claim you are Tapping on their correct dilemma and emotion.

Another way to find a secondary benefit is by asking the right questions. When you think a person has a secondary benefit, ask them upside/downside questions while tapping.

What would be the downside of getting rid of these issues?

Or

What would be the upside of keeping them?

Have them list everything that would change if their problem or belief changed, and then have the person Tap on each of these statements to sense or feel which statement is most true. The process is similar to what you do when there are two aspects and dilemmas, and you are Tapping to determine which topic and/or emotion has the most charge (see Chapter Eight).

Once you learn the secondary benefit, you use the STM to address this new information.

Sometimes a person discovers their secondary benefit and a new aspect or emotion may arise, such as disbelief, embarrassment, anger, or sadness. Whatever is behind the secondary benefit, work through it with STM and the 3As. Particularly watch the SUD levels to discover if you are Tapping on the correct aspect. Give yourself time to develop this skill. It is a complex technique, and your confidence will increase with time and practice.

SECONDARY BENEFIT EXAMPLE: CAREER SUCCESS

Secondary benefits often arose when I was doing career coaching with Tapping. The reasons people did not move ahead were profound and fascinating! Take Paul, for example.

Paul was an advertising copywriter, and he decided he wanted to write a novel. Near the book's completion, he started experiencing writer's block. Nothing changed after we Tapped on why he told me he might have writer's block. He continued to freeze, unable to complete his manuscript indicating a secondary benefit for the stall.

Many people would guess that Paul didn't want to finish his book and get it published because he feared people judging it. However, what we discovered from Tapping is that he did not have a fear of criticism. He had a fear of what success brings. To find Paul's secondary benefit, I used a Tapping technique I call "Leading Phrase: if–then."

Paul was Tapping and repeating what I was saying.

"If I finish my book, I will accomplish my dream.

"I will prove I am a good writer.

"It will allow me to receive money for my efforts.

"I won't be a phony; I will be legitimate.

"I will be successful."

Then I introduced the Leading Phrase to search for a secondary benefit.

Me: "And with this success, I will then..."

Paul: "And with this success, I will be busy."

Me: "And with this success, I will then be busy doing _____." (I pause for him to finish the sentence.)

Paul: "I will be publicizing my book and speaking on the subject."

That's when he froze and looked at me strangely. The *I-Spy* game was over, and Paul had won. Paul realized the reason he didn't want to finish the book wasn't because of a fear of failure or judgment. He feared success because with success came public speaking and social media. If he published his book, Paul believed he would need to speak in public, do book signings, go on podcasts, and do other types of social media. His unconscious mind was keeping him safe. It created writer's block—a reason to freeze.

I have worked with numerous authors struggling with writer's block, and you would be surprised how often there is an unknown secondary benefit to not completing a manuscript.

Paul was astonished and embarrassed but also relieved. Our follow-up Tapping sessions were designed around his fear of social media. Interestingly, by Tapping, he could cognitively appraise his options and identify ones he had never considered. He decided to finish his book but wait to publish it no matter how good it was. This decision to not publish turned off his panic and self-sabotage, which he needed to allow his creativity to flow.

Many people have an unknown fear of failure. However, I found that many professionals also have a fear of success.

Fear gives us a binary perspective, but Tapping
allows us to perceive multiple choices.

Conscious Denial—I Don't Want to Admit a Truth

Sometimes a person contacts me to help them with a problem, but once they begin to grasp the truth beneath the surface, they realize they don't want my help. It becomes clear to them that the truth, for whatever reason, is so undesirable that they consciously work to stop their feelings from rising. I can see on their face that they may sense the unwelcome thoughts.

Once they begin to understand their message, they instantly clamp down and deny any feelings. It's like they are saying, "Nope, we aren't going there." Sometimes they don't want to acknowledge something. As long as they don't admit it, they don't have to do anything about it or change how they feel about something or someone.

If people don't want to admit their true feelings that begin to surface with Tapping, they won't. They will dance around their unwelcomed revelation and say, "Well, I didn't feel anything. Tapping doesn't work for me," and quickly wrap up the Tapping session.

How do I know they deny this revelation? Because at some point in the Tapping, they pause and look at me with an "Oh crap, busted" look or tears well in their eyes. I stop and inquire about the look, and they quickly deny they are feeling anything. Then, they tighten the screw on their memory-and-emotions vault and work hard to continue Tapping without trying to feel anything.

Even though I *know* something is there, it isn't my place to push. Sometimes, people push their unwanted revelation down because they don't want to admit it. Other times, they don't want me to know their truth. Consequently, they never contact me again, even if they paid in advance for numerous Tapping sessions.

This happened with an acquaintance who contacted me to address her chronic pain that started two years earlier. Even though I typically don't work with people seeking pain relief, I agreed since I knew this woman personally. Doctors and specialists couldn't find any reason for the chronic pain that had slowly manifested. Like with Robyn, I asked if an event may have triggered this onset of pain. Her answer was no. So, I suggested we Tap while seeking a past triggering event.

As we were Tapping backward in time to discover if any specific event triggered the onset of pain, she suddenly halted and looked up at me. I asked her if she felt something. She immediately said no, and her expression went flat. At that point, she ended the *I-Spy* game because I had almost spied a painful secret she didn't want me to know. After a bit more Tapping, she said she wasn't feeling anything and thanked me for trying to help her deal with the pain. She abruptly left and never spoke to me again in the circles we frequented or even made eye contact.

Facing specific thoughts or truths may be difficult or even terrifying. However, when we allow ourselves to confront them with Tapping, we cease giving them the power to devastate or fear them controlling us.

Denial is not a river in Egypt.

Hydration—Drink Water

The body runs on its own electricity. Every cell in the body contains water, a good conductor of electricity. Being hydrated keeps communications flowing, allowing for emotional shifts, so I make sure the client is hydrated before every EFT session.

☞ Key Concepts

- Tapping may not work because the emotions used while Tapping are too general.

- Psychological reversal is self-sabotage and often a reason why Tapping appears not to be working.

- Sometimes the effect of Tapping is subtle, so people don't realize it helped with their dilemma.

- If a person doesn't have the emotional capacity to handle the truth of their dilemma, their unconscious survival instinct will block them from this awareness.

- Secondary benefits are the positive benefits we get from not changing our ingrained behavior patterns, no matter how harmful they may be.

- People may pretend Tapping doesn't work because they fear feeling or acknowledging something.

Final Thoughts

What can Tapping help with? Everything!

After having gone through this book, I hope you realize this bold statement isn't such an exaggeration after all. Tapping is a self-regulation, trauma recovery, and diagnostic tool with unlimited applications.

In my years of teaching thousands of professionals how to use Tapping, I've created two simplified Tapping techniques that are less confusing and more practical than traditional EFT while being just as effective.

Functional Tapping (FT) is a convenient treatment tool for self-regulation and grounding. The Simple Tapping Method (STM) is more than a self-regulation tool. STM is an abbreviated version of traditional EFT to uncover past painful memories and events that hold us back from being the best version of ourselves. Ultimately, it helps to relieve us from these harmful or unwanted behaviors. It helps with recovery from trauma. Once you learn FT, you can learn STM quickly and easily adapt these tools to traditional EFT.

We've looked extensively at the benefits you and your clients can expect from Tapping and the science behind it. You've learned fundamental techniques, such as the 3Ts—Tap, Talk, and Tell the truth—and the 3As—awareness, acceptance, and action. We've covered working with trauma and addressing stress and anxiety reduction.

As mental health professionals and educators, you have many tools. Tapping is another tool of proven effectiveness with both professional and personal uses.

If you're like I was, you may still feel I'm overstating Tapping's effectiveness. Whether you believe this or not, I urge you to do what I did: try it for yourself and your clients. You never know; emotional freedom may only be a Tap away.

I wish you, and those in your circle of influence, healing, health, and happiness.

"Yesterday I was clever, so I wanted to change the world. Today I am wise, so I am changing myself."
—*Rumi*

APPENDIX A

Tapping Techniques, Strategies, Glossary, and More

Below are glossary terms and techniques that many practitioners instinctively do when Tapping. I have created my own names for some of them for teaching purposes.

A Part of Me Technique: This technique creates a subtle shift so the client doesn't develop resistance to what is being said and tapped on. It is a way to acknowledge dichotomous thoughts, beliefs, and emotions and have them both be accepted. It is also a way to work with someone who does not want to admit something. By acknowledging both points, I am not creating resistance. If Tapping is all about telling the truth, then we must acknowledge that there might be two truths that are not mutually exclusive. Complex and conflicting thoughts, beliefs, and emotions might be involved.

Example:

- "A part of me believes I am capable, and a part doesn't believe I am capable."

- "A part of me wants to recover from my trauma, and a part of me fears going through the process."

- "A part of me wants to forgive my partner, and a part doesn't."

Argue Tapping: Argue Tapping is just like it sounds. You tap on a negative thought or phrase, immediately followed by a positive one. It trains the brain to replace a negative with a positive.

Borrowing Benefits: This occurs in group Tapping, where the issues or specific emotions of the person Tapping out loud elicit reactions from those tapping along.

Happy Tapping: When you dump the negative words and shift to positive ones to create happier energy.

"I Wonder" or "What If I Could" Technique: This is a Positive Pivoting Phrase to shift from angst to wonder, positivity, or acknowledging our humanness. Example: "What if I can let this go just a teeny bit?"

Leading Phrase and Nudging Words Technique: A Leading Phrase is when you purposely add an audible pause and do not finish a sentence, allowing the client to complete the thought. It is like a nudge to help them make conscious connections.

A couple of leading phrases I often use are:

"If _____ happens or is true, then..."

"Because if I do, then..."

Maintenance Tapping: Tapping homework I give a client to use Functional Tapping to "press pause," break harmful patterns of thoughts, and improve clarity.

Positive Pivoting Phrases (PPP): A type of Happy Tapping. These phrases are used to strategically pivot from negative words and emotions to favorable terms, affirmations, and possibilities.

Public Tapping Technique: Public Tapping isn't actually Tapping at all. It is pressing on the EFT acupuncture meridian points of your choosing to reduce anxiety while in public. If you're a visual learner, watch my video on Public Tapping by searching YouTube using the term "Public Tapping Tijana Coso."

When I have a highly emotional client or one who has been crying on and off, I suggest they stop moving through the Tapping points and switch to Public Tapping Points that are not on the face and, therefore, are more comfortable than circling through all the points.

Rant Tapping: Created by EFT master Marti Murphy, Rant Tapping is a raging version of Tapping and usually entails ranting and cursing (if you swear).

Resistance: At any time during a client therapy session, listen for resistance. A person's resistance or denial can show up in numerous ways: "I'll never get over my trauma," "I'll never get the new job," or "Tapping doesn't work." These beliefs are forms of resistance that block and hinder change and effective therapy. How likely is it that a person will get over something they claim is impossible? They will give more energy to proving and seeking confirmation that their belief is correct than being open to the possibility of change. This is what is known as the "confirmation bias."

To address resistance, use STM.

Example:

1. Label It—Describe the dilemma.

"I don't believe I will ever get over my trauma."

2. Label It—The content.

"I will never get over my childhood trauma because it was so frightening, and I don't want to discuss it. I tried therapy, and it didn't work. Meditation and yoga triggered me, and the medication prescribed puts me in a fog."

3. Label It—The emotion you feel when considering the struggle listed above.

"I fear it is hopeless, and I will never have a normal life."

Use STM and the 3As to work through the belief and resistance. By Tapping on accepting that this is their current belief, you are attempting to lower their SUD score even a tiny bit, moving the needle toward anything other than impossible.

With new clients, I typically begin sessions by addressing resistance and skepticism about the effectiveness of Tapping. While Functional Tapping, I say things like, "This Tapping thing probably won't work," or "I'd like it to work, but how can it work? It looks so weird." I do this to help them become neutral to the possibility of

Tapping working because I don't want them unconsciously straining to resist this possibility. Resistance takes energy away from the ability of Tapping to work.

Safety Litmus Test: If it's unsafe to go into the body and feel or act, your unconscious will discover a way to block you from feeling or acting. The brain is protective and will keep you emotionally safe until you can manage what you are learning.

Sharing and Shaming Phenomenon: It's just like it sounds. A person starts Tapping and sharing, and they eventually shift to shaming themselves for having the feelings they are sharing.

Steering Wheel Tapping: Tapping the Side of the Hand point on the steering wheel while sitting in your car.

Tapping Round: A one-time pass Tapping on each of the eight STM points.

Tapping Script: Verbiage culled from the discovery process.

Tapping Target: The Tapping Target (sometimes called an aspect) identifies the specific issue and emotion chosen for the Tapping Rounds.

Trauma Theme or Theme: A repeated belief/behavior pattern pervasive in one's life.

Trying Shoes On Technique: Introduce different aspects, statements, and phrases to see if they fit and stick.

APPENDIX B

Charts and Graphics

	Traditional EFT	STM	FT
Definition/ Benefits	A self-regulation technique that incorporates exposure, cognitive therapy, and somatic stimulation elements. It alleviates stress and anxiety by tapping or rubbing nine acupuncture meridian points on your face and upper body while focusing on what is bothering you. Traditional EFT aids your physical and mental health by lowering the stress response. It reduces the emotional impact of traumatic memories. It often helps to uncover the core issue causing distress. At times it may elicit strong emotions, so it's not as beneficial to use when you don't have time to work through these emotions.	A simplified version of traditional EFT. I use STM as a foundation to teach traditional EFT.	A simplified version of traditional EFT. I use FT to teach STM and traditional EFT. Used specifically for grounding and self-regulation purposes like you would use a cleansing breath.

	Traditional EFT	STM	FT
How to Perform	**Step One:** Begin tapping on the side of the hand point while stating a phrase called the set-up statement. This statement includes two parts. The first part addresses what you are currently struggling with, and the second part states some form of affirmation. You repeat the set-up-statement three times, all the while tapping on the side of the hand point. **Step Two:** Express or focus on the stressor, and the details surrounding this stressor while continually tapping on the other eight additional EFT meridian points. You repeat this second step numerous times by continuing cycling and tapping on the eight points.	The first step is the same as the second step in traditional EFT. Express or focus on the stressor and the details surrounding this stressor while continually tapping on the other eight additional meridian points. You repeat this numerous times by continuing cycling and tapping on the eight points.	Express what is bothering you while continuing tapping or pressing on one or two traditional EFT meridian points you choose. Typically, a person picks whichever points they feel the most sensations with. Simply Tap, Talk, and Tell the Truth.
When to Use	**Traditonal EFT is a diagnostic and emotional healing tool.** Use traditional EFT to reduce anxiety or reduce influences of painful or traumatic memories by somatically working through them with Tapping.	Same as traditional EFT.	Use to quickly reduce unwanted thoughts and emotions to bring the Thinking Brain back online.

	Traditional EFT	STM	FT
Differences	Requires numerous steps and protocols, so it can be more confusing to learn and not as easily replicated. Continually using the Set-Up Statement can interrupt the flow of the session. When a person is amid strong emotions and visceral, vivid memories, inserting a structured phrase and tapping on it three times can be disruptive and halt the natural flow of the process. There are times when inserting an affirmation before the person has tapped on their anxiety or pain causes them to consciously or subconsciously resist and push back on what is being said, thus creating resistance. With traditional EFT we don't avoid painful thoughts or memories. We lean into and through the pain. So a person needs time to recover from working through strong emotions.	By eliminating the first step, STM is more easily learned and replicated. Without the first step of the traditional EFT protocol, the session can flow naturally and no resistance is created. A person needs time to recover from working through painful memories and emotions.	Since it requires only a couple of meridian points, it is quickly replicated. FT isn't designed to uncover painful memories, so it can be used anytime with no need for processing painful memories or emotions.

Functional Tapping

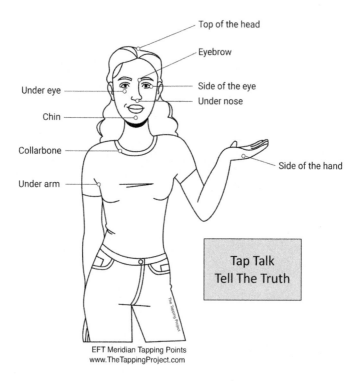

EFT Meridian Tapping Points
www.TheTappingProject.com

1. Feel It -- Begin Tapping at any EFT point. While tapping, move through a couple of your favorite Tapping points while stating audibly or inaudibly what your frustration or dilemma is, including your emotions. If you desire, you can indicate where you feel the sensations in your body. Feel what you are saying. Tap, Talk, Tell the Truth. The goal is to resolve or become less charged and more neutral to the dilemma.

2. Dump It -- End your Tapping session on positive emotions by dumping the negative words and shift (pivot) to affirmations: "I give a voice to this emotion," "I honor my feelings," "I profoundly love and accept all of me;" "I choose to be calm and peaceful."

For Tapping Videos, Search YouTube: Tijana Coso
*Duplication is permitted with attribution given to Tijana Coso
©Feb 2023 Tijana Coso   Tap@thetappingproject.com
www.thetappingproject.com

Simple Tapping Method (STM)
Label It – Feel It – Dump It (LFD) System

1. Label It -- Describe the dilemma. What's bothering you? Finish this sentence: I am struggling with _____

2. Label It -- The content. Write down details and thoughts about the dilemma/stressor. The more specific, the better. Or finish the sentence: I'm struggling with _____(above dilemma) because_____(the details as you see them).

3. Label It -- The emotion you feel when you think of the above struggle. You can pick a general emotion; however, for STM to be most effective, you must uncover a core emotion. If you can't identify a core emotion, it should arise after some Tapping. "When I think of_____(dilemma), I feel___(emotion)."
- Examples of general emotions: upset, frustrated, overwhelmed, anxious, stressed, controlled, sad, unheard.
- Examples of core emotions: anger, fear, resentment, unloved, hurt, abandoned, shame.

4. Feel It -- Create Your Target Statement. Combine dilemma/stressor, emotion and body part: chest, heart, stomach.
Example: "When I think of it_____(above stressor), I feel _____ (emotion). And I feel this ____(emotion) in my _____ (body part)."

5. SUD Score (number) -- Rate the intensity of the emotion you feel from one to ten, with ten having the most charge. Use this as a baseline SUD score, and then, following several Tapping Rounds, compare the current SUD (number) to the initial SUD. A Tapping round is one pass through the Tapping points. Example of a SUD score (intensity number): "My anxiety regarding the new job is an eight."

6. Feel It -- Begin Tapping at any EFT point. While tapping, move through the points while reading the above details, including the emotion and where you feel the sensations in your body. Feel what you are saying. Tap, Talk, Tell the Truth. After several Tapping Rounds, re-state your Target Statement and give it a SUD score. Compare the current SUD to your baseline SUD score. The goal is to resolve or become less charged and more neutral to the dilemma. If new aspects and emotions arise, use the STM to address these.

7. Dump It -- End your Tapping session on positive emotions by dumping the negative words and shift (pivot) to affirmations: "I give a voice to this emotion," "I honor my feelings," "I profoundly love and accept all of me;" "I choose to be calm and peaceful."

For Tapping Videos, Search YouTube: Tijana Coso
*Duplication is permitted with attribution given to Tijana Coso
©Feb 2023 Tijana Coso   Tap@thetappingproject.com
www.thetappingproject.com

Emotional Freedom Techniques (EFT)
Label It – Feel It – Dump It (LFD) System

1. Label It -- Describe the dilemma. What's bothering you? Finish this sentence: I am struggling with_____.

2. Label It -- The content. Write down details and thoughts about the dilemma/stressor. The more specific, the better. Or finish the sentence: I'm struggling with _____(above dilemma) because_____(the details/content as you see them).

3. Label It -- The emotion you feel when you think of the above struggle. You can pick a general emotion; however, for EFT to be most effective, you must uncover a core emotion. If you can't identify a core emotion, it should arise after some Tapping. "When I think of (dilemma), I feel (name emotion). And I feel this (emotion) in my __(name a body part: chest, heart stomach)."

- Examples of general emotions: upset, frustrated, overwhelmed, anxious, stressed, controlled, sad, unheard.
- Examples of core emotions: anger, fear, resentment, unloved, hurt, abandoned, shame.

4. SUD Score (number) -- Rate the intensity of the emotion you feel from one to ten, with ten having the most charge. Use this as a baseline SUD score, and then, after several Tapping Rounds, compare the current SUD (number) to the initial SUD. A Tapping round is one pass through the Tapping points. Example of a SUD score (intensity number): "The anxiety I feel in my stomach regarding the new job is an eight."

5. Feel It -- Create a Set-Up Statement. Repeat it three times while tapping on your Side of the Hand point before beginning the Tapping Rounds. This statement is your dilemma, emotion with a positive affirmation: Even though_____(stressor and emotion) I_____(affirmation)."

- Set-Up Statement example: "Even though I am hurt because ____, I honor my feelings anyway."
- Affirmation examples: I profoundly love and accept all of me, I choose to be calm and peaceful.

Begin the Tapping Round at any EFT point. While tapping, move through the points while reading the above details, including the emotion and where you feel the sensations in your body: "I feel all this hurt in my chest." Feel what you are saying. Tap, Talk, Tell the Truth. After several Tapping Rounds, compare the current SUD surrounding the issue to your baseline SUD score. The goal is to resolve or become less charged and more neutral to the dilemma. If new aspects and emotions arise, use the LFD system to address these.

6. Dump It -- End your Tapping session on positive emotions by dumping the negative words and shift (pivot) to affirmations: "I give a voice to this emotion," "I honor my feelings," "I profoundly love and accept all of me;" "I choose to be calm and peaceful."

For Tapping Videos, Search YouTube: Tijana Coso
*Duplication is permitted with attribution given to Tijana Coso
©Feb 2023 Tijana Coso, Tap@thetappingproject.com www.thetappingproject.com

Additional Reading

Many books enlightened my journey. Here are a few from my favorite authors. I keep a current list at www.TheTappingProject.com under Resources.

Aware: The Science and Practice of Presence, The Groundbreaking Meditation Practice, Daniel J. Siegel

Born for Love: Why Empathy Is Essential—and Endangered, Maia Szalavitz and Bruce D. Perry

Change Your Brain, Change Your Life: The Breakthrough Program for Conquering Anxiety, Depression, Obsessiveness, Lack of Focus, Anger, and Memory Problems, Daniel G. Amen

Sapiens: A Brief History of Humankind, Yuval Noah Harari

Self-Compassion: The Proven Power of Being Kind to Yourself, Kristin Neff

The Body Keeps the Score: Brain, Mind, and Body in the Healing of Trauma, Bessel van der Kolk

The EFT Manual, 3rd ed., Dawson Church

The Inflamed Mind: A Radical New Approach to Depression, Edward Bullmore

The Neuroscience of Change: A Compassion-Based Program for Personal Transformation, Kelly McGonigal

The Polyvagal Theory: Neurophysiological Foundations of Emotions, Attachment, Communication, and Self-Regulation, Stephen W. Porges

The Science Behind Tapping: A Proven Stress Management Technique for the Mind and Body, Peta Stapleton

Waking the Tiger: Healing Trauma, Peter A. Levine with Ann Frederick

When the Body Says No: Exploring the Stress–Disease Connection, Gabor Maté

Acknowledgments

There are specific experiences in my journey that have played a prominent role in shaping my belief systems on how humans think, behave, and direct their lives. These learnings influence how I approach the Emotional Freedom Techniques.

Starting in 1991, my children attended an Association of Montessori Internationale preschool. The director, Alice Crawford, and parents attended child development courses from the Hanna Perkins Center for Child Development to learn social-emotional child development. Parents also received training on the Montessori Philosophy. During parent-teacher conferences, Alice would speak of the child's approach to learning and classroom interactions in the context of the mother-child and father-child relationships. I remember lamenting to her that, upon observing my son Stefan in the classroom, he didn't seem to have any friends. She pointed out that he appeared happy in the classroom. Then she warmly smiled at me and asked, "Who needs friends right now?" I began to cry a bit because she was absolutely right. We had recently moved to the area, and I had no friends or family nearby. I was isolated and lonely. This is when I realized my challenges and past adverse experiences unknowingly influenced how I raised my children. From that point, I keenly considered my approach to parenting. I examined how I raised my children: how I see them, speak to them, and discipline them.

Concurrently, I joined a twelve-step group called Al-Anon. This group supports people who have had or still have alcoholics in their lives, be it a parent, sibling, partner, child, or other person. One of the program's premises suggests that we look at our behavior and how it can affect others. This, too, influenced my parenting. I considered how I parented and why I parented the way I do. Being in the twelve-step group guided me to examine my beliefs about all my interactions and life choices.

One of the tenets I use in my work with Tapping clients is an Al-Anon slogan: there's a payoff to all behavior. I use this premise when I perform the Simple Tapping Method to discover the reason for a particular belief or behavior. Once the person finds their "why," I then use another Al-Anon slogan to address and dissolve their troubles—the Three As: awareness, acceptance, and action. This, too, has become a part of my Tapping process.

I am profoundly grateful to several individuals who supported me throughout my journey of overcoming my trauma and crafting this book.

My four adult children: Stefan, Milan, Natalie, and Neven Junior. Your encouragement and excitement about my ever-changing endeavors gave me the strength to persevere. You have become beautiful, compassionate people making this world a better place. How you conduct your lives inspires me to be a better person, and I honor each of you.

Mom and Dad, you honed my grit and determination. Your many encouraging notes and voicemails pulled me through my life's challenges and supported me along my nontraditional career paths. I know you were a little befuddled with this Tapping endeavor. Even when Dad would jokingly say, "Get a real job," and then tap frantically all over your face, I knew you had my back.

To my siblings, Georgine, Mark, and **MATT**, and my sister-in-law, Mitzi, who always accepted me for who I am and backed me when I needed extra help. Thank you dearly.

To my new family members, my daughter-in-law Ana, granddaughters Nova, Téa, and my soon-to-be son-in-law, Jordan, you enrich our family.

To my sister Georgine, and dearest friends who traveled through the trauma with me and listened endlessly to my fears and hurt: Paul, Paula, Kathy, Robin, Colette, Lizzi, Annette, and Kuma. Aren't you glad less listening is needed now that I have Tapping? To my lovely ladies who helped me begin to fly—the wings.

To the four amazing women who took a substantial amount of time to read my book and offer their editing suggestions: Paula, J. T. H. Chick, Robin, and Jennifer Cox. Your expertise saved me when I was drowning.

A special thanks to a few souls who believed in me and never knew how much it empowered me: Ciara Davis, Connie Smith, Licia Sky, Jody Johnston Pawel, and George Jacinto.

To my EFT heroes, who dared to preserve when few believed: Gary Craig, EFT founder; my teacher Carol Look, psychotherapist and EFT master; Dawson Church, PhD; David Feinstein, PhD; Brad Yates; Nick and Jessica Ortner for taking EFT awareness to another level; Marti Murphy; and Peta Stapleton, PhD. I follow all of you and respect your energy and effort.

Printed in Great Britain
by Amazon

43754571R10126